Individual Centered Behavioral Interventions

A Multimodal Functional Approach

Editors

Dorothy M. Griffiths, Ph.D.
Brock University
Ontario, Canada

William I. Gardner, Ph.D.
University of Wisconsin-Madison
Madison, WI USA

Jo Anne Nugent, M.A.
Nugent Training and Consultant Services
Ontario, Canada

1999

NADD Press, Kingston, NY.

This manual was partially funded through a grant from the NC Department of Health and Human Services, Division of Mental Health, Thomas S. Section and is thus in the public domain and can not be sold within the borders of North Carolina.

Library of Congress Number: 98-067484

ISBN 1-57256-008-8

1st Printing 1998
2nd Printing 1999

Printed in the United States of America

CONTENTS

PREFACE AND ACKNOWLEDGMENTS

Individual Centered Behavioral Interventions represent a positive approach to using behavioral concepts and procedures with persons who have developmental disabilities and also present mental health concerns. The approach recognizes the individual as a unique person who presents many complexities and needs.

Behavioral interventions are derived from an understanding of the multiple biomedical and psychosocial conditions that contribute to a person's challenging behaviors and are designed to assist that person in accomplishing personal goals in a self-enhancing manner. Our individual centered approach is educative in that the major focus is on teaching new skills to increase the personal competencies of the individual. Our approach also is biomedical and ecological in perspective in recognizing that behavioral challenges reflect the interactions between a person's medical and psychological characteristics and his or her numerous physical and social environments. *Individual Centered Behavioral Interventions* focus on three key goals:

- *To improve the quality of life of the individual, with quality being defined by the individual according to his or her personal goals.*

- *To teach appropriate and useful interpersonal, social, coping, and self-management skills.*

- *To minimize or eliminate in a positive and nonintrusive manner those individually unique biomedical and psychosocial conditions that contribute to the challenging behavior.*

These goals are the foundation of our clinical interventions, even for persons with extremely challenging behaviors that create problems for the person and for those in the person's social network.

We strongly support "person centered planning" (Pfadt and Holburn, 1996). We advocate a focus on increasing the person's competencies as a means of addressing problems and skill deficits. We attend closely to the person's goals and aspirations. We understand that the causes of a person's challenging behaviors seldom are primarily within the person, but rather result from a mismatch between the person and his/her environments. Unfortunately, professionals all too often concentrate on providing "special" clinical services in "special" treatment settings that have minimal if any significant relationship to the person's day to day life. In contrast, we believe that our role as professionals is to provide those supports needed to insure that the person can enjoy a high quality of life while residing in the community.

A commitment to the individual centered approach clearly influences our actual methods of clinical practice. You will

find this philosophy illustrated repeatedly in the chapters to
follow. These chapters consist of:

- *Chapter One. Introduction*—a discussion of biomedical
  and psychosocial influences that place the person with
  developmental disabilities at risk for developing challenging behaviors.

- *Chapter Two. Understanding Challenging Behaviors*—
  a description of the three categories of factors that influence the occurrence and habitual recurrence of challenging behaviors, namely, *instigating* conditions, *vulnerability* conditions that places a person at "increased risk,"
  and *reinforcing* conditions that contribute to the purpose-
  fulness or function of these behaviors.

- *Chapter Three. Initiating the Case Formulation Process*—a description of the steps involved in developing a
  set of diagnostic-intervention formulations relating to
  specific challenging behaviors.

- *Chapter Four. Methods of Gathering Assessment Information*—a description of procedures for gathering the
  individual specific diagnostic information needed in the
  case formulation process.

- *Chapter Five. Creating Preventive and Proactive Interventions*—translating assessment information into individual centered biomedical and psychosocial interventions of a preventive and proactive manner.

- *Chapter Six. Creating Habilitatively Appropriate Environments*—creating high quality positive environments for people that support each person in (a) developing personal competencies, (b) minimizing challenging behaviors, and (c) enriching his/her life.

- *Chapter Seven. Proactive Strategies for Management of Challenging Behaviors*—changing antecedent conditions to reduce the need for challenging behaviors and to increase the motivation for appropriate self-enhancing behaviors.

- *Chapter Eight. Teaching Prosocial Skills as Functional Replacements*—using our knowledge and skills to teach new skills as alternatives to challenging behaviors. The desired outcome results both in increased personal competencies and enjoyment of life experiences.

- *Chapter Nine. Training Approaches for Teaching Prosocial Skills*—using behavioral principles to develop step-by-step teaching programs.

- *Chapter Ten. Responding To Escalating Problems*—managing "crisis" in a positive and effective manner consistent with an individual centered philosophy.

- *Chapter Eleven. Creating an Integrated Service System*— working together across services to provide the most effective supports for persons with challenging behaviors.

These Chapters are supplemented with appendices that provide program formats for teaching social and self-management skills. A final appendix provides a Quality Assurance Checklist for the Multimodal Integrated Intervention Plan.

In summary, this book applies the *Individual Centered Behavioral Interventions* approach to the most significant, and often perplexing, aspects of the lives of persons with developmental disabilities and mental health concerns. Our collective experiences have taught us that a positive individual centered approach to challenging behaviors can be effective and enriching for all. We hope that you too will find *Individual Centered Behavioral Interventions* to be useful and positive for the individuals whom you support.

We wish to express our gratitude to Robert Fletcher, Executive Director of the National Association for the Dually Diagnosed, and to Val Carmine, Training Coordinator, Thomas S. Services, North Carolina Department of Human Resources, for providing the encouragement and resources needed to develop this clinical manual. Our thanks are extended to the professionals in North Carolina who provided a valuable critique of earlier drafts of these materials. Judy Ederer and Tracy Martel are given our special appreciation for their invaluable support in preparation of the manuscript.

Dorothy M. Griffiths
William I. Gardner
Jo Anne Nugent   1998

CHAPTER ONE

INTRODUCTION

Dorothy M. Griffiths, Jo Anne Nugent and
William I. Gardner

All of us at one time or another seek to understand the actions of other people that seem puzzling to us.

We want to know *why* specific people in our lives behave the way they do — our children, our spouses, our bosses, our friends. If we understood *why*, it would certainly make our lives easier!

Those of us who work with persons with developmental disabilities confront this question on a frequent basis, especially as it relates to challenging behaviors. We want to provide the best possible supports. Yet challenging behaviors frequently seem to block our attempts to provide those supports that would insure a better quality of life.

We devote a significant amount of time and resources in "managing" challenging behaviors, often with little or no long term improvements. It is our belief that one of the major reasons that such behavior management is ineffective is that it is not based on an understanding of the "causes" or the *why* of these behaviors.

If we thoroughly understand the current features of the person and his/her physical and social environments that determine *why* an individual behaves as he or she does, we would be in a position to design effective ways of changing these influences. And in so doing, we could support the person in selecting alternative ways of behaving that would insure better quality of life experiences.

Chapter Two examines the complex question of *why* people behave as they do. This initial discussion provides the foundation for the chapters to follow in which the practices of *Individual Centered Behavioral Interventions* are described. The reader is encouraged to keep in mind that although the discussion centers on persons with developmental disabilities and mental health concerns, the content is equally applicable to all of us.

Challenging Behaviors And Developmental Disabilities

Why do people with developmental disabilities and mental health concerns frequently present challenging behaviors? Why are the challenging behaviors so often dangerous and seemingly bizarre and inexplicable?

These are questions that people frequently ask.

It is well documented that persons with developmental disabilities often exhibit more disruptive behaviors than their non-handicapped peers. Estimates indicate that between 12% to 15% of persons with developmental disabilities display severe behavior problems such as aggression and self injury. This prevalence rate is reported even higher for persons with significant mental health concerns (Reiss, 1994).

It is important to understand that challenging behaviors are not a fundamental characteristic of developmental disabilities. Rather, the high frequency of challenging behaviors relates to various biomedical and psychosocial risk factors. The following represent examples of these factors.

- *People with developmental disabilities have an increased prevalence of neurological, sensory, and physical abnormalities.* Seizure disorders and other central nervous system abnormalities, as examples, may produce chronically increased autonomic arousal, irritability, organically-based generalized anxiety, and proneness toward rage reactions. Under these biologically-based arousal conditions, the person has decreased potential for coping with external sources of aggravation. Challenging behaviors of an impulsive and agitated disruptive nature are likely results.

- *People with developmental disabilities must cope with lifestyles* that frequently are characterized by restrictiveness, prejudice, limited personal independence, restricted personal control, paucity of mentally healthy experiences, and victimization.

- *People with developmental disabilities have skill deficits in critical functional areas.* These skill deficits make it more difficult to appropriately deal with the stresses of life. As a result, inappropriate behavior are used excessively as attempts to cope. For example, a woman who cannot verbally communicate that she has a stomach ache may scream loudly and persistently. If she had other ways of relating to her pain and of informing us about it, we could remedy the situation. These alternative behaviors would serve the same purpose as the screaming and would thus remove the need to scream. As a second example, a person with moderate cognitive impairment and a depressed mood state may respond aggressively when urged to accompany his group home peers to the day vocational program. If the man had the skills to label his emotional state and indicate to staff that he would prefer to remain at home until he felt better, the aggression would become unnecessary. Of course, if staff were skillful in detecting his depressed mood and in offering support in resolving this distressful internal state rather than insisting that he participate in an activity that at the time was of limited interest to him, the motivation for the aggressive acts also would be eliminated.

• *Persons with developmental disabilities have atypical learning histories.* Often, positive behaviors have not been acknowledged positively and negative and disruptive behaviors have attracted excessive attention. Under these conditions, negative behaviors become predominate ways of insuring that personal needs are attended to by others. In some instances, positive skills have not been taught because of the faulty belief that persons with developmental disabilities could not learn or would have no use for such skills. Also, challenging behaviors may have been tolerated as being "cute" or acceptable in an atypical environmental setting.

These and similar types of conditions and characteristics, individually and in combination, render the person *vulnerable or at risk* for development and repeated use of challenging behaviors.

In summary, individuals with developmental disabilities and mental health concerns encounter more difficulties in living their lives and have a restricted range of personal skills and resources to relate to these difficulties in socially acceptable and personally enhancing ways.

These risk influences are present to a certain degree in the lives of all persons with a developmental disability but are magnified in those who also have significant mental health concerns. It is important to be aware of these risk factors. This awareness will be useful in understanding challenging behaviors and in selecting and providing effective supports for the person.

CHAPTER TWO

UNDERSTANDING CHALLENGING BEHAVIOR

William I. Gardner

As persons who provide personal and program supports, we often wonder, "What should I do when someone acts aggressively? What is the best way to respond to a person who is destructive?"...and the list goes on. There are no specific answers to these and similar questions. There is no pill for aggression or a magic strategy to reduce destructiveness. As emphasized in later discussion, a person's behaviors when viewed separately from the various *contexts* in which these occur tell us nothing either about the causes or how to treat these. Challenging behaviors do, however, have several features in common.

Challenging behaviors often:

- *Appear unpredictable* as to when these may occur,
- *Vary in frequency and severity* across time,
- *Are chronic* and have been present for an extended period of time,
- *May be frightening* and or dangerous to self or others,
- *Appear to be beyond the control* of the person,
- *Are puzzling* relative to the specific situations in which these occur, and
- *Occur across different settings* or situations.

These chronic challenging behaviors typically have been "managed" or "treated" in a number of different ways, but frequently have been resistant to change. As noted earlier, a critical reason for this lack of success in our view is that interventions are not based on an understanding of why the behaviors occur. A number of factors make our understanding of the "why" of behavior difficult. As examples of these barriers:

• *Challenging behaviors seldom occur in isolation.* That is, seldom does a person demonstrate only aggression or only self-injury. Rather, challenging behaviors frequently occur in clusters such as being aggressive, self-injurious, and engaging in episodes of property destruction. These multiple problem areas frequently reflect multiple causes and may require multiple interventions.

• *The manner in which challenging behaviors occur may change over time and across situations.* Aggressive acts, in illustration, may be minor in severity when occurring in the morning hours and quite severe during late afternoon, or may occur following minor provocation in the group home but require major and repeated provocation in the work setting prior to occurrence. This variation may reflect the effects of multiple causes which in turn increase the difficulty of successful interventions.

• *These behaviors, as suggested, seldom are caused by one factor.* Most typically, a number of different conditions influence various of the behaviors at different times and in different situations. As noted, multiple interventions may be needed for successful treatment of the multiple conditions that produce the challenging behaviors.

The challenging behaviors most likely to require formal intervention programs are those of physical aggression, threats of violence, self-injury, property destruction, chronic social disruption, agitation, pica (eating inedible objects) and excessive negative or uncooperative behavior. These behavioral challenges, when viewed in isolation, tell us nothing about what causes the behaviors or what behavioral supports are needed. These challenging behaviors have been described as *"nonspecific behavioral symptoms"* because when viewed in isolation are not specific in any cause or set of causes (Gardner, 1996).

To elaborate, the term *"nonspecific"* means that challenging behaviors (e.g., aggression, self-injury) are not categorically the result of any specific cause but rather may be produced by a variety of conditions. An analogy in physical medicine would be the presence of a headache. A headache is a nonspecific physical symptom because in isolation it is not indicative of any particular physical cause. Rather, a multitude of physical ailments may result in a headache, just as a variety of biomedical and psychosocial conditions can influence occurrence of a nonspecific behavioral symptom such as aggression.

The term *"symptom"* is used to emphasize that any challenging behavior is a "symptom of," that is, the end result of or produced by, some other conditions. The primary target of individual centered interventions thus must be the *conditions that produce the challenging behaviors* rather than the behavioral symptoms themselves. That is, a challenging behavior such as aggression or property destruction does not represent the direct target of intervention efforts. We must "look beyond" these behavioral symptoms and seek to identify, and modify, the conditions that account for their occurrence. Although, due to their severe destructiveness, disruption, or danger to self or others, the challenging behaviors may need to be managed or controlled with various temporary measures, just as a headache can be managed temporarily with aspirin. These symptoms, however, will occur again in the future unless the causes are modified or eliminated.

In summary, to report that someone is aggressive tells us nothing to assist in understanding the factors influencing this challenging behavior.

A Biopsychosocial Perspective For Understanding Challenging Behavior

As is obvious to all of us, the challenging behaviors of persons with mental retardation and mental health concerns typically are rather complex and not readily understood. An integrated approach that recognizes the possible joint effects of biomedical, psychological, and social/environmental influences on challenging behaviors is described in this Manual. An integrated approach means that we combine, or integrate together, information about various aspects of the person and his/her physical and social worlds. With this integrated approach, we minimize the problem of "behaviorizing" challenging behaviors that have a major medical or psychiatric basis or "medicalizing" other challenging behaviors that have a primary pychosocial basis. The following vignette illustrates this benefit:

Mr. Wills Irving, with a dual diagnosis of mental retardation and schizophrenia, currently resides in a group home in the community. A recent increase in his aggressive outbursts resulted in an injury to one of the home support staff. Under the assumption that the mental illness caused the violence, medication dosage was increased but had no positive results. A multimodal contextual assessment, however, suggested that the major influences for the increase in frequency and severity of aggression were psychosocial rather than psychiatric in nature. It was discovered that a new support staff, under the belief that his duties included that of insuring that all men in the group home attend all scheduled programs, persistently prompted Wills to attend a community outing that he did not wish to attend. As Mr. Irving's verbal refusals had been ignored, he expressed his aggravations through becoming physically aggressive. As the aggression was effective in accomplishing his purpose of avoiding programs that he did not like, these outbursts became more frequent. When staff repeatedly prompted him to attend program, the aggressive outbursts became more intense.

In this scenario, the mental illness represented at best only a minimal influence on the increase in aggressive episodes. Staff behavior was identified as the major source of instigation of this challenging behavior. The intervention program shifted from medication to a focus on changing staff approaches and on providing related coping skills training for Wills. Specifically, after removing staff provocation, the intervention focus shifted to increasing the attractiveness of scheduled programs. Additionally, Wills was taught coping alternatives to aggression as means of expressing his aggravations.

An integrated *biopsychosocial* perspective is described in this training manual (Gardner & Sovner, 1994). The view stresses an integrated systems approach to challenging behavior and recognizes that such behavior is the end result of conditions representing differ modalities of influence. The *bio-* modality refers to biomedical (physical, psychiatric, and neuropsychiatric) conditions. The *psycho-* modality refers to psychological characteristics of the person. The *social-* modality refers to features of the physical, social/interpersonal, and program environments in which the person resides and experiences. This perspective also emphasizes that each of the three *modality of influence* affects and is affected by every other modality. To illustrate these interactions:

Psychiatric conditions such as schizophrenia or a bipolar disorder may result in changes in cognitive functions, mood and affective states, emotional regulation, and psychomotor behaviors. These changing psychological and physical characteristics may result in new behavioral or emotional difficulties or may influence occurrence or increased severity of challenging behaviors that predated a current psychiatric episode. These symptoms in turn create more than usual changes in the manner in which the social environment responds to and interacts with the person and his/her challenging behaviors. These experiences with the social environment may in a reciprocal manner reinforce the challenging behaviors or intensify the emotional arousal and the person's perceptions of social feedback. As examples, a person's depressive symptoms such as crying or complaining of physical ailments may be strengthened by the social feedback that these produce. Interventions to be most effective must be

> sensitive to these reciprocal interrelations, and provide attention to each set of influences. Illustrations of this integrated treatment approach are provided in later chapters.

In sum, this perspective indicates that the combination of influences account for the *occurrence, severity, variability, and persistence* of challenging behaviors. This multimodal perspective represents a central component of a Multimodal Contextual Behavior Analytic Model that we shall use to develop our understanding of the "why" of challenging behaviors.

This Model suggests that any challenging behavior is best viewed as the joint effects of a person (with physical and psychological characteristics) in interaction with physical, social/interpersonal, and program environments. This dynamic process may be illustrated as follows:

$$CBs = (re)\ P \Leftrightarrow E$$

CBs refers to challenging behaviors,

= (re) denotes that any occurrence of a challenging behaviors results from,

P refers to a person's current *biomedical* (physical, psychiatric, and neuropsychiatric) and *psychological* features,

⇔ denotes the dynamic interactions between features of the person and features of the environments, e.g., a person without alternative coping skills may engage in a bout of self-injurious face slapping when exposed to a noisy environment only when in a highly irritable mood state. Exposure to the noisy environment when not highly irritable does not result in self-injury. In this example, neither the irritable mood nor the noisy environment in isolation is sufficient to produce the challenging behavior.

E denotes the physical, social, interpersonal, and program features of the person's environments.

As is evident, behavioral supports can be individual centered only to the extent that these supports are derived from an understanding of the multiple influences that in combination result in the challenging behaviors. Again, knowing that the person is aggressive does not provide us with sufficient information about the conditions involved in producing a particular aggressive outburst. It is necessary, as described below, to "lodge" the aggressive behavior in the *multiple contexts* in which it occurs.

Without a clear understanding of what is producing the behavioral "symptom," interventions frequently become reactive or hit and miss in nature. If we went to a physician because of a nonspecific stomach pain, we would insist that any treatment provided would be based on *diagnostic formulations* about what was causing the pain. To arrive at these diagnostic hunches about causes, various examinations and laboratory tests would be completed. Specific

treatment offered would be those logically related to these diagnostic findings. Thus the physician develops a *diagnostic-treat-
ment formulation* that guides selection of the specific treatment
offered.

Similarly with challenging behaviors, the initial step following
description of the behavior is that of gathering information that
will assist us in formulating diagnostic hunches about factors that
appear to contribute to occurrence, severity, variability, and
recurrence of the challenging behavior. These diagnostic hunches
are gained by examining the various *contexts* in which specific
challenging behaviors occur.   Just as the physician examines
various physical or bodily systems to determine the location and
nature of factors that may contribute to the stomach pain (e.g.,
context of an ulcer, context of excessive smoking and eating foods
with high acid content, context of liver pathology), an analysis of
challenging behaviors in the three contexts of (a) *instigating*
conditions, (b) *vulnerability* conditions, and (c) *reinforcing* conditions is completed.   Each of these contexts represents a focus of
analysis.   Each is described in Chapter Three.

What this *Multimodal* (bio-psycho-social modalities) *Contextual*
(contexts of instigating, vulnerability, and reinforcing conditions)
Behavior (focus of analysis is on the "why" of the nonspecific
challenging behavior) *Analytic* (analysis of multiple factors as
potential sources of influence on occurrence, severity, fluctuation, and durability of the challenging behavior) *Model* tells us is
that the concept of "cause" is complex. To emphasize, it is quite
rare that we would find just one reason such as "gets social
attention" or "is schizophrenic" to explain someone's challenging
behaviors. Usually, current influences from several areas of a
person's current life (e.g., impoverished social environment,

minimal social skills, heightened emotional neediness following move of a long-term friend), each serving specific roles, jointly affect that person's challenging behaviors.

This is of particular relevance in the case of a person with a developmental disability and chronic and severe challenging behaviors. We must investigate multiple facets of the person as he/she interacts with social and physical environments on a daily basis to understand what is "causing" the behaviors.

To summarize, each person with challenging behaviors is quite unique. Each has his/her own physical and mental health characteristics, personalities, families, specific environments, and .... the list is extensive. These become the individualized total package that makes each person unique in the factors that influence his or her challenging behaviors.

CHAPTER THREE

INITIATING THE CASE FORMULATION PROCESS

William I. Gardner

Before we look more closely at the three contexts of *instigating*, *vulnerability*, and *reinforcing* influences in search for person-specific conditions that may contribute to a person's challenging behaviors, brief review is offered of a case formulation process that provides a map for us to follow from our initial step of defining a challenging behavior through the final step of evaluating the effectiveness of our supports in enhancing the quality of life of the persons served.

This *case formulation process* represents an adaptation of an age old problem solving method (Gardner, 1996). In selecting individual centered interventions, our initial step is to determine what is happening and why. In formal terms, this is called developing *diagnostic formulations, hypotheses, or hunches.*

After devising these *diagnostic formulations* about why a challenging behavior is occurring, a set of related *intervention formulations*, as suggested earlier, are developed.

Following implementation of the interventions, results of an evaluation of the effectiveness of these may suggest changes in our initial diagnostic formulation and/or in the interventions. The

Case Formulation Process involves the following nine steps.

• Step 1: *Describing* the challenging behavior(s).

• Step 2: *Gathering* diagnostic information through multimodal assessment of the challenging behaviors in the contexts of instigating, vulnerability, and reinforcing conditions.

• Step 3: *Forming* hunches (hypotheses) about the current medical, psychological, and social-environmental "causes" of specific challenging behaviors, i.e., developing *diagnostic formulations.*

• Step 4: *Describing* specific program objectives relative to the "causes" identified in Step 3.

• Step 5: *Developing* a set of *intervention formulations* that address the hypothesized "causes" of the challenging behaviors.

• Step 6: *Selecting* an integrated set of individual centered interventions based on specific diagnostic-intervention formulations. To illustrate the difference between this step and the previous one, assume that assessment of a person's disruptive episodes results in a diagnostic hypothesis that this challenging behavior produces valued staff and peer attention (Step 3). This diagnostic formulation leads to the logically related intervention formulation "meet the person's need for attention in a proactive manner as a means of removing the motivation for the challenging behavior" (Step 5). This general intervention strategy would next be translated into individual centered approaches such as, (a) minimize attention following disruptive behaviors, (b) provide social attention following a range of prosocial behaviors that the person currently exhibits, (c) provide frequent noncontingent personal attention, (d) teach appropriate ways of soliciting attention, and (e) enrich the person's opportunities for positive social interactions with peers and staff.

* Step 7: *Developing* a *staging* plan for providing the various interventions, i.e., deciding on what interventions should be implemented initially and the sequence or timing of the remaining interventions.

* Step 8: *Devising* and *implementing* procedures for evaluation of the effectiveness of interventions.

* Step 9: *Modifying* hunches (hypotheses) and/or interventions based on evaluation results. This step continues until program objectives are met.

As a brief illustration of this case formulation process, let's consider a young adult who is disruptive in her Community Integration Skills program. Gathering further information, we discover that she is throwing her books, yelling at her teacher, and refusing to remain in one particular instructional program that involves teaching the value of money. With additional information, we find that she has not previously acquired even rudimentary money skills and that she does not have basic arithmetic skills. We hypothesize that the subject is too difficult for her and she is expressing her frustrations through her disruptive behavior. As an initial intervention, she is provided the option of joining another group of peers who are learning

basic arithmetic skills and using these skills to acquire
money skills. Her disruptive behaviors disappear. To
prepare her for future stressful encounters, a coping skills
training program of teaching alternative means of expressing frustration would follow.

Although this example is quite uncomplicated, it illustrates the
process of looking beyond the challenging behavior and addressing the conditions that influence its occurrence.

This clinical manual places considerable emphasis on this process
of *looking beyond the challenging behaviors* and gathering information to assist us in developing a set of individual centered
diagnostic-intervention formulations. If these formulations are
not thoroughly and accurately completed, specific interventions
are likely at best to be ineffective and could in fact be inconsistent
with the individual centered philosophy articulated in this clinical
manual.

Understanding Challenging Behaviors In Its Various Contexts

In brief review of the previous discussion, any challenging behavior potentially reflects the effects of biomedical, psychological,
and/or socioenvironmental conditions. These conditions serve
one or more of the following roles in influencing occurrence and
persistent recurrence of challenging behaviors: *instigating* role,
vulnerability role, or *reinforcing* role. These roles are related in
the following manner:

- It is evident to all of us that challenging behaviors do not occur randomly or haphazardly. Challenging behaviors are selective and purposeful in that these occur only when certain instigating conditions are present. A behavior such as aggression does not occur continuously. Rather, a person behaves aggressively only under certain conditions of instigation such as when taunted by peers or when repeatedly directed by staff to engage in activities that the person does not like. As illustrated extensively in the following sections, these stimulus events that serve to signal occurrence of specific challenging behaviors may represent a wide range of biomedical, psychological, and/or socioenvironmental conditions.

- These antecedent stimulus conditions gain instigating influence or control over challenging behaviors as these represent signals to the person that specific challenging behaviors will produce specific reinforcing effects or consequences, that is, will *produce positive consequences* and/or will *remove, reduce or avoid currently present or anticipated negative conditions*. After experiencing this sequence of *Antecedents* - challenging *Behavior* - reinforcing *Consequence* (ABC sequence) on a few occasions, the challenging behaviors become *functional* for the person, that is, serves the function or purpose of producing these effects.

- When exposed to various antecedents, a person with developmental disabilities and mental health concerns may be at increased risk or be vulnerable to engage in the challenging behaviors rather than other acceptable coping behaviors due to various personal and environmental deficits (e.g., coping skill deficits, communication skill deficits, limited program stimulation) and/or pathological features (e.g., allergies that produce psychological distress during pollen season, chronic schizophrenia that occasionally results in delusional thoughts). To illustrate this latter personal feature:

> Mr. Braddock may become aggressive toward a staff member who insist that he attend meals during times that he has the delusional belief that the food is poisoned. The aggressive behavior under these conditions may become functional in terminating the staff directive that he attend meals. Mr. Braddock enjoys his meals when he is free of this psychotic symptom.

Modification of the deficits and pathologies that place the person at increased risk for engaging in challenging behaviors becomes a major program focus of *Individual Centered Behavioral Interventions.* In the example of Mr. Braddock, medication for the delusional thoughts would be provided. Following successful intervention, the delusional view of food as posing a danger to his health would be eliminated as would his aggressive behaviors following prompts by staff to attend meals. This challenging behavior would become nonfunctional in the absence of the delusional belief as Mr. Braddock would no longer be motivated to avoid "poisoned " food.

- Even though challenging behaviors become functional in producing specific reinforcing effects, we should not assume that the person is *aware of or knows* how the behavior became attached to antecedent instigating conditions.

- Likewise, we should not assume that the behavior represents intentional or planned acts. The reinforcing effects of various consequences occur automatically, and frequently are beyond the person's awareness that he or she is learning to be aggressive, or self-injurious, or to destroy property, or to tantrum following occurrence of certain antecedent instigating events. When a person is asked following occurrence of challenging behaviors, "Why did you destroy your roommates tape?" or "Why did you hit Jon in the face?" a common reply is "I don't know." The person on most occasion is being honest in this reply as most challenging behaviors are developed slowly over a period of time during which the behaviors have resulted in reinforcing consequences. With each reinforcing experience, the preceding behavior gains strength and becomes more habitual or automatic on future exposure to similar antecedent instigating conditions. Thus, behavior may appear to be *beyond the control of the person, impulsive,* or *automatic* in nature. In view of this, it serves no useful purpose to blame the person for the challenging behaviors until we provide an individual centered behavioral interventions program that systematically teaches alternative coping skills and personal accountability.

- Although the "cause" of some challenging behaviors may be beyond the person's awareness or control, it is evident that on some occasions these behaviors may be quite deliberate, planned, and intentional. The behaviors also may occur even though the person has alternative prosocial behaviors available in this or her repertoire. In this scenario, the person may be said to "choose" the challenging behavior rather than prosocial ones as a means of gaining specific desired consequences.

With this brief review, we now turn our attention to a more detailed description of the various steps in the *case formulation process.*

Step 1: Defining the Challenging Behavior(s)

The first step in the *case formulation process* involves defining the challenging behavior(s) seen as problematic. This definition should represent an accurate description easily understood by all who are involved with the person. This definition includes specific concrete details to insure that everyone is able to identify an occurrence of the challenging behavior(s) in question.

If we report that a person is aggressive, we are being too general. There is considerable room for individual interpretation. Rather, we describe the actual activities involved such as, for example, hitting another person with an open or closed hand along with some description of severity.

Why is clarity of definition important? It ensures that assessment information has a common reference point. If several staff are keeping records about when and how often an individual engages in aggression, we want them to be consistent in what they are observing and reporting. If one person records a light slap on a person's arm as aggression while another staff thinks that the slap is too weak to be recorded, we would not obtain consistent information that would be of value in the assessment process.

At the beginning, we may not even be sure what the actual problem is. We may have received reports that the person is acting out or being difficult, without any more specifics. If this is the case, it may be helpful to use general checklists to define the problem areas. Some checklists which might be considered are the Aberrant Behavior Checklist (Aman, Singh, Stewart, & Field, 1985) and the Reiss Screen For Maladaptive Behavior (1988).

Defining the behavior should include thorough and clear descriptions of the following:

The behavior itself—this is a general statement of the behavior such as aggression, or self-injury, or attention seeking, or screaming.

The topography of the behavior—the actual activities which can be observed such as "Joan bites her hand or fingers."

Some measure of behavior strength—various indicators such as the *frequency* or number of times the behavior occurs within a specified time period (e.g., the aggressive behavior occurred 11 times last week), *severity* of behavioral episodes (e.g., each episode poses a danger of injury to self or others), and/or *duration* of an episode, (e.g., his screaming episodes continue for an average of 10 minutes before he quiets down).

The social and physical situations in which the behavior occurs—the situation(s) in which the behavior occurs and is viewed as unacceptable. Some behaviors such as self-injury and physical aggression that potentially threatens the physical safety of self or others would be viewed as unacceptable in any situation. Other behaviors such as loud verbalizations would be viewed as unacceptable in some situations and not in others.

After the initial definition of the behavior of concern, a basic question is raised: Should we intervene in the situation at all? After all, each person has the right to some idiosyncrasies. Just because someone has a developmental disability does not suggest that perfect behavior should be expected from the individual. Therefore, before initiating a time consuming assessment of the instigating, vulnerability, and reinforcing contexts in which a behavior occurs, we initially should decide if the behavior in question is clinically significant or whether we should just accept the behavior and respect the person's right to it.

Griffiths (1989) suggested that any behavior is defined as a problem not by its nature, but by looking at factors associated with the behavior. These factors are frequency, severity, and duration. We would thus intervene if the behavior fell outside of the boundaries such that:

• The frequency, severity, and/or duration of the challenging behavior are significantly outside what is culturally acceptable and/or,

• The challenging behavior occurs with people, in places, at times, or in situations that render it significantly outside the social norm and/or,

• The behavior infringes upon the health, well being, or property of the person or others and/or,

• The behavior seriously interferes with the person's development or interactions and/or,

• The behavior impedes the learning of new skills that could greatly improve the person's quality of life and/or,

• The individual recognizes that the behavior is in need of change and seeks assistance in the change process.

In sum, assessment and intervention are justified only if the challenging behavior is having a serious negative impact on the person's quality of life, is threatening the well being of the person or others, and/or if the person seeks assistance in changing the behavior.

Step 2: Gathering Diagnostic Information

After definition, the next step in the *case formulation process* involves gathering diagnostic information through assessment of the challenging behaviors in the contexts of *instigating, vulnerability,* and *reinforcing* conditions. The Multimodal Contextual Behavior Analytic Worksheet presented in Figure 1 depicts these three areas of assessment. Note that the bio-psycho-social modalities are analyzed in *each* contextual area. Each cell in the worksheet is defined and illustrated in the remaining sections of this chapter. Methods of gathering the assesement information needed for developing diagnostic formulations are included in Chapter Four.

Context One: Instigating Influences

Definition of Terms

Instigating conditions refer to those stimulus events that signal occurrence of challenging behaviors. Terms used for these antecedent instigating events include "cue," "prompt," "discriminative event," "primary instigating event," "setting event," "establishing operations," "secondary instigating event," "priming event," and "triggering event," although these terms differ somewhat in the technical and descriptive meanings offer by various writers. In this manual, antecedent conditions that influence the occurrence of challenging behaviors, that is, *instigating condi-*

		Context 1: Instigating Conditions		Context 2: Vulnerability Conditions	Context 3: Reinforcing Conditions	
		Triggering	Contributing		Positive	Negative
Environmental	Physical					
	Social					
	Program					
Psychological	Present Features					
	Deficit Skills/ Features					
	Medical					
	Psychiatric/ Neuropsychiatric					

Figure 1: Multimodal Contextual Behavior Analytic Worksheet

tions, are defined as representing two subclasses of events, namely (a) *triggering* stimulus conditions and (b) *contributing* stimulus conditions. In formal behavior analytic terms, *triggering events* are called discriminative stimuli and *contributing events* are called establishing operations or setting events. As the terms *triggering* and *contributing* are more descriptive, these have been selected.

The term *"triggering"* denotes that the a person's challenging behavior does not occur unless these specific antecedents are present. At any given time for a person, a specific triggering event, or as described later, a stimulus complex that serves as the triggering condition, has a certain degree of control or influence over specific challenging behaviors. This influence may range from minimal to 100%.

To illustrate:

One adult in a transition community vocational setting may respond in a loud threatening manner *on every occasion* of being provided corrective feedback by the work supervisor. Corrective feedback thus has 100% control over loud threatening behavior. In this instance, corrective feedback represents a triggering condition that, on each time it is provided by staff, serves as a sufficient instigating antecedent for occurrence of verbal threats.

Another person may also respond in a threatening manner to corrective feedback but do so with less frequency and intensity. Staff corrective feedback in both instances serves as a *triggering* instigating condition. However, for the first adult, staff feedback as noted was a *sufficient* stimulus condition to produce the threatening behavior on each and every occasion. With the second adult, corrective feedback, while triggering threatening behaviors on some occasions, was not sufficient on most occasions as an instigating condition for this behavior.

Mr. Jens provides an additional example:

A staff prompt for Mr. Jens to get up in the morning and prepare for work invariably produces loud threats of violence if not left alone. In this instance, the triggering event (staff prompt) represents a *sufficient* stimulus event to produce the threatening behavior.

Of importance also is the observation that any particular challenging behavior such as aggression may be under the instigating influence of *more than a single triggering* stimulus event. In illustration, Gardner, Cole, Davidson, and Karan (1986) reported that a young man attending a day vocational training program engaged in verbal aggression following specific triggering events. Although the challenging behavior *never occurred* unless one of the following antecedents were present, no specific antecedent always resulted in verbal aggression:

• staff reminder of a scheduled program activity,
• staff corrective feedback,
• repeated staff prompts to participate in a program activity,

- staff directives to engage in a specific behavior, and
- teasing, taunting, or verbal threats from peers.

In summary, a specific challenging behavior such as aggression does not occur in the absence of triggering stimulus events *unique to each person* but does not always occur in the presence of any specific stimulus event unless an invariant 1-1 relationship exist.

The second subclass of instigating conditions is referred to as *contributing* conditions. These are defined as stimulus conditions that, when present at the time of occurrence of a triggering event, increase the likelihood that the challenging behavior will occur following that triggering event.

In some instances, an antecedent event (e.g., taunts from peers), while a necessary condition, is not sufficient in isolation to produce a specific challenging behavior unless combined with a contributing event. The following illustrates this influence:

Mr. Snarr may threaten staff when prompted to prepare for program attendance but only on those mornings following a seizure during the previous night. In this instance, the threatening behavior results from the combination of staff prompt plus a psychological state of irritability related to the seizure activity and loss of sleep. Staff prompt results in threats *only* when combined with the irritable mood. Both are *necessary* but neither is *sufficient in isolation* to produce the challenging behavior. The sufficient instigating condition thus represents a *stimulus complex* consisting of a combination of both the staff prompt *and* the irritable mood.

One of the authors, in describing a stimulus complex as an instigating condition, has found it useful to use an analogy involving a rifle. The gun powder in the rifle shell represents a necessary condition for the bullet to fire as does the act of pulling the trigger of the gun. Although the shell is set or primed to fire and propel the bullet, the shell will not fire until the trigger is pulled. Nor will the shell fire after the trigger is pulled unless gun powder is present. Consider an aggressive act as a bullet in flight, a person's irritable mood state as the loaded shell, and a taunt from a peer as the pulled trigger. To continue the analogy, the aggressive act is a result of:

> pulling trigger + loaded shell ⇒ bullet fired
>
> taunt + irritable mood state ⇒ aggressive act

In this illustration, the taunt from peer *and* the irritable mood state comprised the instigating (necessary and sufficient) stimulus complex resulting in the aggressive act. Neither was sufficient in isolation to produce the aggression. To emphasize, even though the presence of both were *necessary* for the aggression to occur, neither was *sufficient* in isolation from the other to produce the aggression. In this instance, the aggression could be managed completely by removing *either* the peer's taunts *or* the irritable mood state as both in combination comprised the necessary and sufficient instigating conditions. Individual centered treatment (consisting of teaching the person to cope with the taunts even when in an irritable mood state) could be added to this management approach to increase the person's independence in self-managing prosocial behaviors when confronted with future instigating conditions such as taunts or other conditions of aggravation.

In other instances, a *contributing event* may not be necessary to produce a specific challenging behavior but may serve to increase its likelihood of occurrence when a triggering event is presented.

Ms. Bledsoe provides an example of an antecedent serving this role as a contributing instigating condition:

With Ms. Bledsoe, challenging behaviors may have a 60 percent likelihood of occurring when, for example, he is directed by staff to engage in a nonpreferred tasks. On these occasions, staff directive is a sufficient triggering event for the behavior. Ms. Bledsoe is cooperative 40 percent of the time with these directives. When Ms. Bledsoe is experiencing menstrual discomfort, the likelihood of occurrence of the challenging behavior following these staff directives increases to 90 percent. However, the challenging behavior never occurs in the absence of staff directives to engage in a nonpreferred task even when menstrual discomfort is present. In this instance, the menstrual discomfort is *neither sufficient nor necessary* for the challenging behaviors, but does serve a *contributing* role in increasing the likelihood of occurrence of the challenging behavior following staff directives (the triggering event). This conditional probability (**cp**) relationship may be depicted as follows:

- staff directive ⇨ challenging behavior = **cp** 60%
- staff directive + menstrual discomfort ⇨ challenging behavior= **cp** 90%

These two classes of antecedent instigating conditions are depicted as follows:

Instigating Conditions

|
_____
| |
Triggering   Contributing

To summarize, the specific types of influence of these two classes of instigating conditions over occurrence of *specific challenging behaviors* are as follows:

• For an individual, a specific triggering event such as a taunt from a peer or staff corrective feedback may result in an act of aggression *each time these occur.* In this instance, the triggering event (i.e., taunt or staff feedback) represents a necessary and sufficient instigating condition.

• For another individual, a specific triggering event such as taunt from a peer, although one of a number of necessary antecedents for an act of aggression for that person, may not be sufficient *on each and every time* taunts occur to produce the challenging behavior (i.e., taunts = aggression on some occasions; taunts = behaviors other than aggression on other occasions).

• For another individual, the instigating condition for a challenging behavior may represent a *stimulus complex* consisting of at least two events (e.g., taunts *and* pain associated with a headache). Both may be necessary but neither the peer taunt nor the pain in isolation represents a sufficient condition to instigate the behavior (e.g., taunts never produce aggression; headache never produces aggression; taunts + headache frequently result in aggression).

• For other individuals on some occasions, an antecedent event such as a migraine headache is neither a necessary nor a sufficient instigating condition for a specific challenging behavior. The psychological distress associated with the migraine, however, may serve to increase the likelihood of occurrence of a challenging behavior when combined with a triggering event (e.g., headache never produces aggression; taunt sometimes produces aggression; headache + taunt frequently result in aggression).

Modality of Instigating Conditions

Instigating events that signal the occurrence of challenging behaviors may have their origin in the external physical, social, and/or program environments or may represent covert or internal psychological and biomedical (medical and/or psychiatric/neuropsychiatric) conditions.

Stimulation arising from any of these external or internal sources may serve either a triggering or a contributing instigating role in producing challenging behaviors. These are summarized as follows:

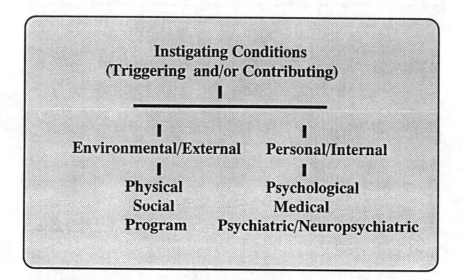

Instigating: Physical Environment

Certain aspects of the physical environment can instigate specific challenging behaviors in individuals with developmental disabilities. When you know someone well, you can probably predict when something will annoy the person so much that he/she will act out inappropriately.

Features of the physical environment which may serve as triggering and/or contributing instigating conditions for challenging behaviors include the following types of conditions:

*   sensory elements such as noise, smells, poor quality air, uncomfortable temperatures, lighting, and humidity,
*   disruptions, frequent relocation, and frequent changes in the physical environment,
*   limited environmental sensory stimulation,

- limited physical space,
- uncomfortable furniture and/or equipment.

This is only a partial list of the multitude of elements which make up the physical environment in which we live. Each individual element could be sufficiently aversive to an individual with a developmental disability to serve as an instigating condition for challenging behaviors.

The reader should note that these same factors are offered as vulnerability conditions in later discussion. These aspects of the physical environment do not continuously produce current stimulus states that are aversive to all persons. However, these do increase the likelihood that a person, when exposed to these environmental conditions, may find these sufficiently aversive to engage in challenging behaviors that in turn may become functional in removing or reducing these.

Instigating: Social Environment

Although aspects of our physical environments may be significant in influencing occurrence of challenging behaviors, even more important are the social elements — that involving other people. As with the physical environment, aspects of the social environment may also *instigate* challenging behavior. In fact, most instigating conditions for challenging behaviors are located in various features of a person's social environments.

A partial list of social factors that could serve a triggering and/or contributing influence for challenging behaviors includes:

- the presence of a specific person,

- an argument with a peer,
- teasing by a peer,
- reduced social attention,
- a tone of voice,
- being stared at,
- disapproval,
- being requested or instructed to do something,
- the visit (presence) of a parent,
- a change in staff, and
- close physical proximity to other peers or staff.

The list is endless! However, you may already recognize some of these as being definite instigators for the challenging behaviors of people you know.

One of the editors has worked with a young man who lived in a group home. This young man physically attacked one specific male staff member. Whenever he saw this male staff, the individual would leap on him and start punching. Other staff would physically remove him away from this male staff. The individual was never aggressive to any other person. In this case, the presence of this particular male staff served as a sufficient instigating event for the aggression. After several years of this behavior, the young man's father reappeared on the scene. The father, who reportedly had been very abusive to the young man, looked exactly like the male staff who was the punching bag!

Instigating: Program Environment

Many persons with challenging behaviors and significant mental health concerns have difficulty self-initiating activities when in environments with minimal structured programming. This lack of structure or absence of planned activities may result in boredom or other negative psychological states that serve as instigating conditions for challenging behaviors. Other examples of program conditions that may serve an instigating role include:

- Frequent changes in routines such as chores, work tasks, bus schedule, and the like,
- Unpredictable changes in expected positive consequences such as meals, activities, and scheduled times for smoking,
- Excessive leisure time with minimal opportunities available for activities that would be enjoyable to the person,
- Inappropriate reinforcement schedule in work environment, and
- Excessive program structure which allows limited periods of unstructured time.

Instigating: Psychological Conditions

A number of personal features of an individual may serve an instigating influence on challenging behaviors. A person who is fearful of thunderstorms may engage in challenging behaviors if instructed to put the garbage in the detached garage during an impending storm. A person in a state of heightened sexual arousal may engage in inappropriate sexual activities. Again, these personal characteristics represent current stimulus states that contribute to occurrence of challenging behaviors.

The reader should recognize that these current states are closely related to personal vulnerability features discussed in the next section. For example, a person may have a personality trait of suspiciousness. However, this personal trait does not continuously produce a heightened state of readiness and perceptual rigidity in interpreting the intent of the actions of others. When around strangers, this perceptual set may be activated and thus serve as a contributing instigating condition for occurrence of challenging behaviors such as inappropriate hostile aggression.

Instigating: Medical Conditions

A wide range of medical conditions may produce psychological stimulus conditions such as pain, discomfort, or irritability that in turn may serve an instigating influence on challenging behaviors. These medical conditions include, as examples, headaches, menstrual discomfort, pain associated with middle ear infections, itching associated with skin disorders, constipation, indigestion and tooth infection. Again, the psychological distress resulting from these and a plethora of other physical ailments may serve a triggering or contributing instigating role (Gardner & Whalen, 1996).

This relationship is illustrated by Brown, Gardner, and Davidson (1998), O'Reilly (1995), and Peine et al. (1995).

In the Brown et al. (1998) study, a correlation was reported between presence of menses and sleep deprivation among adults with mental retardation and an increased occurrence of aggression, self-injury, and episodes of agitated screaming and crying. These challenging behaviors had a higher frequency under triggering stimulus conditions such as staff directives when these medically-related contributing conditions were present than when these were absent.

In a further illustration:

O'Reilly (1995) observed that rates of aggression of a 31-year-old man with mental retardation when provided directives from family members and staff in both home and vocational settings were higher following periods of sleep deprivation than following periods of no sleep deprivation. The stimulus state associated with sleep deprivation served as a contributing stimulus condition that combined with the directives to produce the aggressive acts. Peine et al. (1995) reported an increase in such pre-illness behaviors as self-injury, self-stimulation, and noncompliance and the occurrence of a range of acute medical conditions.

It is well known that most types of medications have side effects. In some cases, the side effects involve aversive stimulus states that may serve to instigate problem behaviors. Various drugs may lead to emotional states such as depressed mood, agitation, or pain.

As one example, akathesia, produced by various psychiatric medications and characterized by an agitated restlessness which includes anxiety and overactivity, may
serve as instigating conditions for challenging behaviors.
A second example is offered by Bailey and Pyles (1989)
who describe a person who began poking his ear following
being given medication that in some persons causes tinnitis.
Withdrawal of the medication resulted in disappearance
of the ear poking.

In those instances in which a challenging behavior occurs in
persons with various medical illnesses or drug induced psychological states, it should not be assumed that the abnormal medical
conditions always produce, that is, serve as sufficient instigating
conditions for, these nonspecific behavioral symptoms. This
becomes evident even with casual observations. Even though
some persons presenting severe earaches, seizure disorders, allergies, or other medical illnesses or pathologies may engage in
challenging behaviors, others with similar medical conditions do
not. On some occasions, various aberrant stimulus components
produced by the illness or dysfunction may indeed serve as
contributing but not *necessary* instigating conditions. In other
instance, these stimulus components may function as necessary
conditions for occurrence of the behavioral symptoms. As noted
previously, however, even in these instances only infrequently
can it be assumed that these stimulus features represent sufficient
features in isolation from specific psychosocial conditions to
produce the behavioral symptoms.

These observations suggest that medical treatment of a person's physical illness may indeed be effective in reducing or eliminating the primary symptoms of the illness but be ineffective in reducing the person's challenging behaviors unless features of these medical conditions (e.g., pain or discomfort) contribute to the stimulus complex producing these challenging behaviors.

Instigating: Psychiatric/Neuropsychiatric Conditions

Recall that instigating conditions refer to a current active stimulus state that precedes occurrence of a challenging behavior. With this definition in mind, a psychiatric disorder such as schizophrenia, a post traumatic stress syndrome, or a depressive disorder does not serve as an instigating condition for challenging behaviors. Rather, current stimulus conditions associated with such psychiatric disorder symptoms as hallucinations, dysphoric mood, or a sudden surge in anxiety resulting from a flashback may represent instigating conditions for a challenging behavior episode.

Symptoms of psychiatric and neuropsychiatric disorders or dysfunctions resulting in psychological conditions that may serve as instigating stimulus states for challenging behaviors include:

- *Cognitive symptoms* such as delusional thought patterns, manic cognitive state, flights of ideas, and pressured speech,

- *Perceptual symptoms* such as visual, auditory, and tactile hallucinations,

- *Mood/Affective symptoms* such as anxiety, anger, apprehension, dysphoria, euphoria, fear, irritability, overarousal, pain, and emotional agitation,

- *Motoric symptoms* such as restlessness, akathesia, aversive stimulus states produced by overactivity and aimless pacing, and

- *Somatic symptoms* such as rapid pulse, headaches, indigestion, and muscular aches.

Specific diagnostic activities are selected to identify, or at least hypothesize about, these *currently active* symptoms of psychiatric and neuropsychiatric disorders, dysfunction, or pathologies as potential instigating influences for challenging behaviors.

These psychiatric symptoms may serve three roles as instigating conditions for nonspecific behavioral symptoms, namely, (a) as sufficient conditions, (b) as necessary but not sufficient conditions, and (c) as contributing conditions that are neither necessary nor sufficient. Each is described and illustrated.

Occasionally, currently active psychiatric features such as hallucinations or a ligh level of anxiety may serve a *sufficient* instigating role. The following provide illustrations:

> Mr. Johanssen was found by his group home parent hiding in his closet. He reported that the sheriff was searching for him and would put him in jail because he had killed his mother. Psychiatric evaluation revealed an active delusional thought disturbance as one component of a schizophrenic illness. The belief that the sheriff was searching for him represented the sufficient instigating condition for the behavior of hiding in the closet. Management of the delusional thoughts through medication would remove

the instigating condition for the closet hiding behavior. Even though this psychiatric symptom (delusional thoughts) was eliminated with medication, Mr. Johanssen continued to have a diagnosis of schizophrenia. This observation supports the previous statement that challenging behaviors are not caused by a psychiatric disorder but rather are influenced in occurrence by some currrently active symptoms of the disorder.

As a second example, Ms. Fran Morman, with profound cognitive impairment and without language skills to communicate his needs, may be provoked to autoaggressive ear slapping by a high level of psychological distress associated with a major depressive illness.

In these examples, the psychiatric symptoms (delusions and highly aversive affective state of distress) served as sufficient instigating stimulus conditions for the closet hiding and autoaggression independent of any additional instigating provocation from external social or physical influences. Effective treatment of the underlying stimulus condition (delusional thought pattern, dysphoric mood) would remove these instigating conditions and the associated challenging behaviors.

In other instances, current psychiatric stimulus features must combine with other antecedents to produce a stimulus complex that triggers the behavior. In this scenario, the current psychiatric stimulus features are *necessary but not sufficient* in isolation to instigate the challenging behaviors. Lowry (1994), Lowry and Sovner (1992), and Sovner, Foxx, Lowry, and Lowry (1993) illustrated the instigating role of such internal psychological states as anxiety, irritability, and dysphoria associated with various psychiatric disorders of mood.

These clinicians described the co-occurrence of episodes of nonspecific behavioral symptoms of aggression and autoaggression and various affective states associated with depression or rapid cycling bipolar disorders. In persons with mental retardation diagnosed with a rapid cycling disorder, occurrence of the challenging behavioral symptoms was dependent on the presence of the psychological state associated with the psychiatric disorder *plus* occurrence of various staff prompts, even though different external prompts served as components of the instigating stimulus complex during different phases (depression or mania) of the disorder. During depressive episodes, staff prompts *intended to get the person involved* in an activity produced the problem behavior. During manic episodes, prompts *to slow the person down or focus attention* produced the behavioral symptom. These prompts, even though necessary conditions, were not sufficient in the absence of the mood state to instigate the nonspecific behaviors. Both the staff prompt and the mood state formed the stimulus complex that represented the necessary precursors for the challenging behavior symptoms. Again, neither was sufficient, independent of the other, to produce these behaviors.

Interventions resulting in the removal of either of these necessary components of the stimulus complex (mood states *or* the prompts) would effectively manage occurrence of the behavioral symptoms. The obvious focus of intervention, nonetheless, would be that of eliminating the aberrant mood states that rendered staff prompts as aversive conditions to be removed or avoided through use of the aggression or autoaggression. Following successful medication treatment of the bipolar disorder and removal of the associated instigating stimulus conditions (i.e., aberrant mood states), elimination of the challenging behavioral symptom would coincide with the concurrent reduction in the aversiveness of staff prompt.

In most instances, aberrant psychological states associated with psychiatric disorders represent *contributing* stimulus conditions that in isolation are neither sufficient nor necessary to produce autoaggression, aggression toward others, or other challenging behavioral symptoms. These contributing conditions serve to influence the likelihood of occurrence of the challenging behavioral symptom when additional necessary conditions of provocation are presented (Gardner et al., 1986). In this *state-exacerbated* relationship, the behavioral symptoms predate the psychiatric illness and increase in frequency and/or severity on occasion of the illness. In this instance, instigating features of the psychiatric disorder combine with additional sources of provocation to increase the likelihood that the behavioral symptoms will occur, but in isolation these psychiatric features are neither necessary nor sufficient as instigating conditions. Effective treatment of the psychiatric disorder would result in only partial reduction of the challenging behavioral symptoms.

To summarize, psychological states produced by a psychiatric illness serve various roles as instigating conditions for nonspecific behavioral symptoms. On some occasions as illustrated in Table 1a, various aberrant stimulus components resulting from the illness may serve as *contributing* instigating conditions.

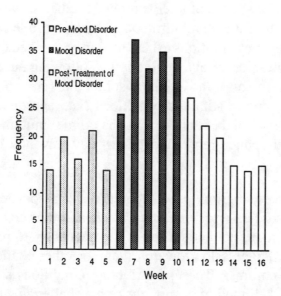

Table 1a. Symptoms of a psychiatric illness serving as a contributing instigating condition for challenging behaviors.

In other instances as depicted in Table 1b, these stimulus components may function as *necessary* conditions for occurrence of the behavioral symptoms. In this case, a *state-dependent* relationship between the psychiatric symptoms and the challenging behavior is present. That is, occurrence of this behavior is dependent upon the presence of the psychiatric state. However as noted in Table 1c, even in these instances, only infrequently can it be assumed that stimulus features resulting from the psychiatric illness represent *sufficient* conditions in isolation from various psychosocial conditions to produce the behavioral symptoms.

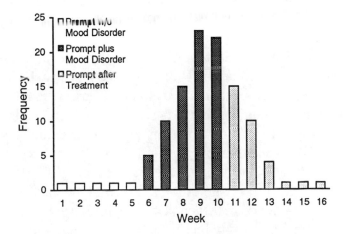

Table 1b. Symptoms of a psychiatric illness serving as a necessary, but not sufficient, instigating condition for challenging behaviors.

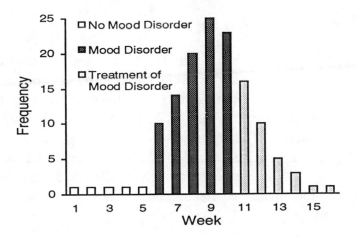

Table 1c. Symptoms of a psychiatric illness serving as a sufficient instigating condition for challenging behaviors.

That a psychiatric disorder always is a sufficient condition is not supported by the observation that even though some persons presenting, for example, schizophrenia or depression may engage in a nonspecific behavioral symptom, others with similar conditions will not. Thus we must look for the *specific symptoms* (e.g., hallucinations, dysphoria, irritability, delusions) of such psychiatric illness or neuropsychiatric dysfunction as schizophrenia, depression, or brain injury that may serve as instigating stimulus conditions. Treatment of a person's psychiatric illness may indeed be effective in reducing or eliminating the primary symptoms of the illness but be ineffective in reducing the person's challenging behavioral symptoms unless symptom features of the psychiatric disorder do in fact contribute to the stimulus complex producing and maintaining these challenging behaviors.

Context Two: Vulnerability Influences

Definition of Terms

Vulnerability influences refer to those (a) personal features of a *psychological (e.g.,* anger management, communication, or coping skills *deficits*) and *biomedical* (e.g., sensory, neurological, or biochemical *impairments or dysfunctions*) nature in addition to (b) those features of the *physical, social, and program environments* (e.g., limited opportunity for sensory or social stimulation, restrictions in the type and frequency of structured program activities) that place the person at *increased risk* for challenging behaviors.

The same category of conditions that represent instigating conditions may also serve as vulnerability influences:

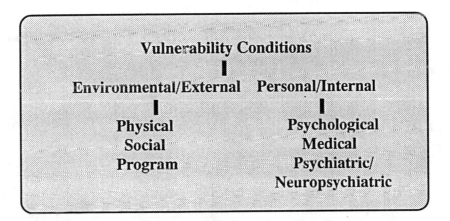

Vulnerabilities Reflecting Physical Environmental Conditions

Recall the previous discussion of physical environmental conditions that serve as potential instigating condition. These same conditions may represent vulnerabilities as exposure to these occasionally may create sufficient psychological distress or other aversive states that in turn may serve an instigating role in influencing occurrence of challenging behaviors.

Vulnerabilities Reflecting Social Conditions

Numerous aspects of the person's social environments can serve as vulnerabilities for challenging behaviors. Examples of these include:

- Abusive family, staff, and peers,
- Demanding family, staff, and peers,
- Social environments that provide infrequent positive feedback, and

• Social environments with inadequate staff and peer models.

These and similar social conditions not only hold potential for presenting numerous instigating and reinforcing conditions for challenging behaviors but also may inhibit the development of the range of prosocial behaviors and motivational/emotional personal features critical to desired interpersonal and social adaptation.

Vulnerabilities Reflecting Program Conditions

Recall the previous discussion of program conditions that serve as potential instigating condition. These same and similar conditions also may represent vulnerability influences. Exposure to these conditions occasionally may result in active stimulus conditions that serve an instigating role for challenging behaviors. These include:

• Frequent changes in routines such as living area, chores, work tasks, bus schedule, and the like,
• Unpredictable changes in expected positive consequences such as meals, activities, smoking schedule,
• Excessive leisure time with minimal opportunities available for activities that would be enjoyable to the person,
• Inappropriate reinforcement schedule in work environment,
• Limited environmental stimulation, and
• Excessive program structure.

Vulnerabilities Reflecting Psychological Conditions

As we know, individuals with developmental disabilities have skill deficits in a number of critical areas related to successful community living. Such skill deficits may increase a person's *vulnerability* to displaying challenging behaviors. The absence of or limited ability to perform certain skills may lead to the person being unable to cope positively with the complexities of a community lifestyle.

For example, let's consider a man who frequently is teased by another man at the vocational program. When teased, this individual becomes aggressive and punches the teaser. This man may lack the skills to deal with his tormentor in a socially acceptable manner. Lacking these skills, he resorts to aggression which in turn stops the teasing but leads to additional difficulties for him. If we teach alternative ways to respond to the teasing, he is likely to cope more effectively with the situation. We may teach him such strategies as moving to another part of the workshop away from his teaser or asking the teaser to stop.

Certain skill deficits consistently appear as major vulnerabilities in persons with a developmental disability. Some examples are lack of ability to problem solve, limited anger or anxiety management skills, limited or nonexistent verbal communication skills, low tolerance for stress, and limited social, vocational, and leisure skills.

As one example, persons with developmental disabilities may use challenging behavior that we do not usually associate with communication to tell us what they need or want. A person may become aggressive whenever he has a headache and is directed to engage in an activity that involves a noisy and crowded setting. Someone else may occasionally become self-injurious to escape from a disliked peer. This is unfamiliar to us because we expect people to use their words to tell us if they are ill or do not want to participate in an activity. However, if words are not an available tool, or if others do not attend to the person's verbal communication, the person may learn to use challenging behavior to get needs met.

In addition to skill deficits that increase the person's risk of challenging behavior under various conditions of provocation, various personality characteristics and motivational features may represent vulnerabilities. As described earlier, a person may have a personality trait of suspiciousness that, under certain social conditions, may result in misinterpretation of the intent of a peer who offers to share his box of candy. If the peer persist in his attempts to be charitable, aggressive behavior may result.

Motivational features of the person may represent distinct vulnerabilities. Examples of these for many persons with mental health concerns include:

*   numerous aspects of the social and physical environment represent cues for negative emotional arousal,

*   a person may have a restricted range of activities, objects, and events that have positive reinforcement value,

*   specific activities, persons, or objects may be excessively sought after or excessively avoided and serve as a major source of motivation for the person's challenging behavior,

*   immediate reinforcement is required too frequently, and

- the person is excessively dependent on others to provide reinforcement.

As is evident, a major focus of *Individual Centered Behavioral Interventions* is on reducing the psychological vulnerabilities of the persons with challenging behaviors and mental health concerns.

Vulnerabilities Reflecting Medical Conditions

Any medical condition that, on a cyclic basis, produces psychological distress (e.g., pain, irritability, fatigue) that could serve as instigating conditions for challenging behaviors places a person at risk for occurrence of these behaviors.

For example, a person with a seizure disorder may become highly irritable prior to seizure activity. This irritability may serve as a contributing stimulus condition that, when combined with a triggering event such as an unwanted directive from a peer, results in a verbal tirade. As seizure activity may be partially controlled by medication, the seizure disorder, although a vulnerability feature of the person, may only occasionally be involved in influencing verbal aggression. The seizure disorder places the person at risk for challenging behaviors during those times that irritability results from seizure activity. At all other times during which preseizure activity is not occurring, and is not producing irritability, this vulnerability feature is "dormant" relative to instigating conditions and at that time does not produce psychological states that may serve as instigating influences for challenging behaviors.

Ms. Libert provides a second illustration:

Ms. Libert is an older adult with chronic arthritis who presents aggressive outbursts on an episodic basis. The chronic arthritic condition serves as a vulnerability influence for these challenging behaviors. This medical condition (vulnerability influence) results periodically in acute inflammation and resulting severe pain. Aggressive behavior is likely to occur when the pain level is high (contributing stimulus state) *and* a peer invades her personal space. These two stimulus conditions in combination serve as the sufficient instigating condition. During periods of time of either freedom from pain or sufficient pain reduction, the same peer intrusions routinely result in a prosocial coping response rather than aggression. Knowledge of this vulnerability influence suggests various medical interventions, namely, use of medication either (a) to reduce the acute pain episodes once these occurred or (b) as a medication maintenance strategy that routinely treats the inflammation and thus consistently keeps the pain at a low level. If successful, these medical interventions would remove the periodic pain-related psychological distress that formed a critical element in the instigating stimulus complex producing the challenging behavior.

The following case study by Gardner and Sovner (1994) provides a third illustration of a medical condition that served a vulnerability role.

Mr. Peete, a person with profound cognitive impairment and minimal communication skills, presented episodes of agitation, aggression, and self-injury. The absence of functional vision due to detached retinas rendered Mr. Peete vulnerable to heightened anxiety/fearfulness when exposed to crowds and loud noises. Under these conditions, he was unable to visually process his surroundings and as a result became fearful due to the unpredictable nature of the intent and actions of peers in this setting. Records revealed a history of his being the target of both inadvertent and intentional physical assaults by peers. The heightened anxious arousal served as a contributing stimulus condition that resulted in episodes of aggression and self-injury when confronted with various triggering events such as being accidentally jostled or even approached by an excessively noisy peer. In sum, while not instigating the challenging behaviors, the sensory limitation represented a major vulnerability influence in a large percentage of his episodes.

Vulnerabilities Reflecting Psychiatric/ Neuropsychiatric Conditions

A number of personal features associated with psychiatric disorders render a person at risk for engaging in nonspecific behavioral symptoms. In persons with a mood disorder, such symptoms as the fluctuating intensity of mood states, the mood lability, increased likelihood of physical fatigue associated with sleep disturbances, energy loss associated with eating difficulties, and aberrant activity levels all increase the likelihood of aversive states of psychological distress. Various writers have suggested that these aversive psychological states "lower the threshold of responding," thus rendering the person more likely to engage in aberrant behavior under other conditions of provocation (Coccaro, 1989; Thompson, Egli, Symons, & Delaney, 1994). These combine with a broad array of psychological coping skill deficits to further increase the likelihood of occurrence of challenging behavioral symptoms. In sum, any psychiatric or neuropsychiatric disorder may represent a vulnerability condition. When these disorders result in active psychiatric symptoms, stimulus features of these may serve as instigating conditions for challenging behaviors.

Context Three: Reinforcing Influences

Definition of Terms

As suggested in previous sections, challenging behaviors come under the influence of preceding instigating conditions based on what happens following ocurrence of the behavior. Challenging behaviors increase in likelihood of being repeated (i.e., gains in strength and thus becomes functional or purposeful) to the extent that these behaviors result in reinforcing consequences. The challenging behavior may result in *positive consequences* (viewed as positive from the person's perspective) or may result in the *removal, reduction, or avoidance of negative conditions* (viewed as negative from the person's perspective). These two reinforcing processes are called *positive reinforcement and negative reinforcement*. This reinforcing process may be depicted as follows:

Challenging Behavior ➡ reinforcing consequences =
⇑ behavior strength.

Positive reinforcement = behavior results in consequences that the person enjoys, finds valuable, seeks, is
motivated to obtain, finds rewarding, or positive.

Negative reinforcement = behavior results in the removal,
reduction, or avoidance of present or anticipated conditions that, from the person's perspective, are aversive,
painful, unpleasant, unwanted, uncomfortable, or negative.

The sources of reinforcement may involve both environmental
and personal features:

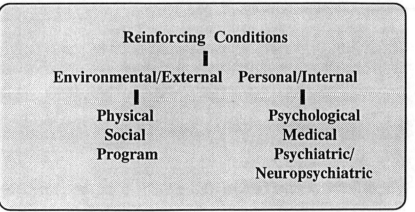

Reinforcing Conditions
❚
Environmental/External   Personal/Internal
❚   ❚
Physical   Psychological
Social   Medical
Program   Psychiatric/
Neuropsychiatric

Physical Environmental: Reinforcing Influences

Removal, reduction, or avoidance of any of the aversive physical environmental conditions described earlier may serve to reinforce preceding behaviors. In a similar manner, behaviors that result in positive environmental conditions such as increased personal space, desired temperature, or a quiet environment may be strengthened.

Social: Reinforcing Influences

Numerous aspects of the social environment may serve as reinforcing conditions for both challenging and prosocial behaviors. The specific behavioral consequences that serve as positive or negative reinforcers, of course, vary from one person to another. Potentially, any feedback of a social nature may serve to reinforce challenging behaviors. In a similar manner, removal, reduction, or postponement of unwanted social contact or feedback may serve as reinforcing consequences. It also is of interest that some persons with developmental disabilities and mental health concerns may be reinforced by aggravating others or by producing signs of distress in others. Careful attention should be paid to the effects of various consequences on a person's behaviors rather than deciding what *should be* reinforcing to the person.

Program: Reinforcing Influences

A variety of program conditions can produce reinforcing effects. A person may engage in an agitated outburst in response to a training program that is boring or otherwise aversive to him or her. Removal from the program would serve to strengthen the challenging behavior. In our experiences, persons with developmental disabilities and mental health concerns frequently are scheduled for programs that have minimal if any positive reinforcement value to the person. Challenging behaviors, under these conditions, may become quite functional in escaping from, delaying, or avoiding exposure to these experiences.

> This can be seen, for example, in a work environment when an individual engages in aggression towards peers whenever his work team does a particular type of job that he dislikes. If this aggression results in his being removed from the work setting, he will learn that aggression serves the purpose of removing him from a job he dislikes. This behavior is likely to be repeated on future occasions of being exposed to this job.

Psychological: Reinforcing Influences

As noted, positive or negative reinforcers are quite individually and personally defined.

> For example, a person with a developmental disability who is emotionally distraught over the severe illness of a parent may be extremely disruptive during dinner preparation when staff are busy getting the meal ready. At this time of the day, staff may be too busy to interact with the individual. However, when the individual acts out, various staff always approach the individual and comfort him.

Under these circumstances, the disruptive behavior serves
the function of obtaining attention, even though momen-
tarily, to his emotional distress.

Some behaviors such as self-stimulation and self-injury have been
identified as providing sensory stimulation for some people with
developmental disabilities. This sensory stimulation is presumed
to be reinforcing. Therefore, these challenging behaviors may
serve the function of providing valued stimulation (Gardner &
Sovner, 1994).

Medical: Reinforcing Influences

Any behavior that provides relief from pain or other distress
resulting from medical conditions may be strengthened. To
illustrate:

Slapping one's ear can temporarily modulate the pain of
an earache. Likewise, a person who is in pain from being
in a wheelchair for several hours may "act out" in order to
be put to bed. This may seem like a punishment to a
caregiver but the change in body position results in pain
relief for the individual.

Psychiatric/Neuropsychiatric: Reinforcing Influences

Occurrence of challenging behavioral symptoms may result in

changes in the internal affective, cognitive, and perceptual states associated with various psychiatric disorders. These changes may contribute to the strength and functionality of the behavioral symptoms. As illustrations, responding aggressively may remove a staff directive to attend a scheduled training program rendered aversive by a dysphoric mood state; self-injurious face slapping may become functional as it results in frequent personal attention in a person who becomes excessively emotionally needy during periods of sadness. In these instances, the challenging behavioral symptoms become more likely in the future when exposed to similar instigating conditions as these have resulted in consequences valuable to the person.

How Factors Interact

When we discussed each of the individual factors, we gave examples that demonstrated one factor and its relationship to a behavior. In reality, many of our examples were too simple. More typically, a number of factors interact to account for the occurrence, fluctuation, severity, and persistence of most challenging behaviors of persons with developmental disabilities.
The relationship usually looks like this:

> Mr. Fontaine's concern about losing his girl friend results in a state of angry agitation. At this time, staff may begin to insist that he "hurry and get dressed because the group is leaving for the ball game in 5 minutes." Mr. Fontaine is in no mood to accompany the group but is told that he must go because there is no available staff to remain with him. This increases his agitation level. One of his peers begins to push him toward the bus which produces an

aggressive reaction. Finally, one of the staff decides that
Mr. Fontaine is too upset to go and remains at home with
him.

In assessing "why" the aggressive behavior occurred, several
factors must be considered:

worry $\Rightarrow$ angry agitation (*contributing event*) + push from
peer (*triggering event*) + limited anger management skills
and related coping behaviors (*vulnerabilities*) = aggressive responding $\Rightarrow$ removal of directive to go with the
group (*reinforcing consequence*).

As a second example,

We can look at the situation of a woman known to suffer
from migraine headaches. When she has a migraine
headache, asking her to complete her nightly hygiene
routines always results in her having a tantrum which
includes screaming at staff, throwing objects, and kicking
walls. Once she tantrums, she is removed to her room for
the night, without completing the hygiene routines. We
can see different levels of factors at work here in influencing the tantrum outbursts.

The medical disorder of migraine headaches represents a *vulnerability*. When headaches occur, the woman is likely to be bothered by elements in her environment. The request to carry out the nightly hygiene routine combines with the headache to produce a sufficient *instigating stimulus complex* for the tantrum. The tantrum serves the function of avoiding the unwanted hygiene routines (*negative reinforcement*).

To review, the headaches make her less likely to cope with any pressures, requests, and stresses. However, on their own, the headaches do not result in a tantrum. The request to carry out a task in combination with the headache instigate the tantrum. The request must occur before there is a tantrum. However, the woman would not tantrum at such a request if she did not also feel physically ill. Once she does tantrum, she then avoids the activities which she has less tolerance for when she is ill. We see how the combination of conditions are interrelated. A pattern is woven in which the factors impact on each other.

Final Thoughts

At first, this multidimensional way of looking at behavior may seem too difficult to you — but, do not panic! It becomes easier as you begin to think in the multimodal contextual mode.

CHAPTER FOUR

METHODS OF GATHERING ASSESSMENT INFORMATION

William I. Gardner

With these definitions and illustrations of each component of the Multimodal Contextual Behavior Analytic Worksheet as background, discussion now turns to a brief description of some assessment procedures for obtaining the information needed to complete Step 3 of the Case Formulation Process. This step involves the development of diagnostic hypotheses to account for correlations or covariations between challenging behaviors and specific biomedical and psychosocial events or conditions. These diagnostic formulations represent an essential base for guiding the development of an effective *Multimodal Integrated Behavior Intervention Plan* (Figure 2). Current discussion is restricted to Column A (Diagnostic Hypotheses) of this Plan. Note that this column represents a summarized integration of the information obtained through use of the *Multimodal Contextual Behavior Analytic Worksheet* (Figure 1). Description and illustration of the remaining columns of this Plan, representing Steps 4-9 of the Case Formulation Process, are provided in Chapter Five.

Clinical Descriptive Assessment

Methods of gathering initial assessment information include the

Multimodal Integrated Intervention Plan

Name: _____

Date: _____

Staff: _____

Target Symptoms

1. _____
2. _____
3. _____

	(A) Diagnostic Hypotheses	(B) Program Objectives	(C) Diagnostically-based Interventions	(D) Staging Plan	(E) Expected Change (Type/magnitude/ time)	(F) Data (Type/Schedule)	(G) Responsible Staff; Review Schedule
Environmental Formulations							
Psychological Formulations							
Medical Formulations							
Psychiatric Formulations							

Figure 2: Multimodal Integrated Intervention Plan Format

use of (a) unstructured interviews and informal direct observation and (b) systematic direct observation in the person's natural environments. Description and illustration of these procedures follow.

Useful diagnostic information about potential instigating, vulnerability, and reinforcing influences may be obtained initially (a) from unstructured written or verbal accounts provided by the person presenting the challenging behaviors and by others who have first hand experience with the individual presenting the challenging behaviors and/or (b) through informal or unstructured direct observation of the person in the various situations in which the challenging behaviors occur. These other persons providing the narrative accounts may include parents and others in the individual's place of residence as well as staff in educational, vocational, therapy, recreational, and other program settings. Initial inquiry is guided by questions about the time, location, and personal/environmental contexts of the behaviors. During this inquiry, attention is focused on instigating antecedents as well as the potential positive and negative reinforcing consequences resulting from the behaviors. In addition, the variability of the behaviors under specific conditions, (e.g., "When I ask him to attend to his work") would be explored. To illustrate the potential value of this line of inquiry, it may be reported that agitated/disruptive episodes appear more frequently following staff directives when the person is "in a bad mood" or "doesn't seem to feel good." Such information would suggest an increased likelihood of the disruptive episodes when psychological and biomedical stimulus states are combined with staff directives.

Additionally, informants are asked if the person has engaged in appropriate behaviors under similar circumstances in the past. This line of inquiry is designed to identify possible skill and motivational limitations or differences that may serve as personal vulnerabilities.

These narrative accounts may be followed by or coincide with direct observations of the person in those situations in which the challenging behaviors are reported to occur. Information gained during these initial unstructured interviews and informal observations provides a basis for (a) formulating operational definitions of the target behaviors and (b) selecting a more structured assessment format in which initial impressions concerning antecedents and subsequent events become specific items of formal inquiry. This may consists of a formalized direct observation format. A more structured format is useful as information obtained through less systematic procedures may result in an overestimation of both the frequency and severity of challenging behavioral episodes.

Gardner and Sovner (1994) describe a procedure for obtaining more systematic observational data. A small index card, depicted in Table 2, is used by an observer to record each incident of the target behavior as or shortly after it occurs. The cards would be completed by observers naturally present in the various locations in which the challenging behaviors occur. The observer records the *Date and Time* of occurrence, *the Situation* (e.g., lunch, gym, work), antecedent *Triggering Events* (e.g., I suggested that Susan wait until lunch for food that she requested.), *Challenging Behavior* (e.g., Susan began yelling and swinging out at me.), *Consequences* (e.g., I redirected her arms and talked to Susan in a calming manner), and *Possible Contributing Instigating Influences*. In this last section, the observer describes any additional environmental or personal conditions that appear to contribute to the person's challenging behaviors (e.g., Susan has been highly irritable throughout the morning. Usually present during her menses.).

NAME: _Mr. John T._   OBSERVER: _D. Ford_   DATE: _3/14_

                                          TIME: _2:15 p.m._

SITUATION: _Walking with group of peers to grocery store._

TRIGGERING EVENTS: _Joel bumped into John and pushed him off the sidewalk._

BEHAVIOR: _John immediately began face slapping and screaming._

CONSEQUENCES: _Held his arm. Reassured him that Joel would not push him again. Calmed after 30-45 seconds._

POSSIBLE CONTRIBUTING INSTIGATING INFLUENCES: _Insisted that I walk with him until he arrived at grocery store. Noticeably apprehensive and cautious when Joel approached him._

Table 2: Completed Data Recording Card

Following a 2-3 week observation period (time period varies depending upon the frequency and representativeness of pattern of occurrence), the resulting index cards are initially sorted into categories based on the type of antecedent instigating conditions recorded. Following this initial analysis, the cards are next sorted into categories based on the recorded consequences produced. In this manner, (a) descriptions are obtained of various antecedent triggering and contributing conditions and (b) hypotheses are developed about the motivational basis for the person's challenging behaviors. This analysis provides one or more hypotheses relating to instigating conditions, possible vulnerabilities, and reinforcing consequences.

In this analysis, it is not unusual to find that specific challenging behaviors of a person is motivated at various times by such different consequences as social feedback, escape from specific situations viewed as aversive by the person, and acquisition of specific tangibles. In frequent instances, as demonstrated by a number of functional analysis studies, a predominate source of motivation typically becomes evident for an individual, with other conditions assuming less significance as sources of impetus for a person's challenging behaviors (Carr & Durand, 1985; Smith, Iwata, Vollmer, & Zarcone, 1993). The resulting motivational hierarchy, in illustration, may identify escape or avoidance from various aversive conditions as being of most significance, with social consequences of less significance.

In frequent instances, a specific motivational condition will be associated with multiple instigating conditions. In illustration, a person's escape-motivated self-injury may be associated with such different instigating conditions as instructional demands, taunts from peers, an intense state of dysphoria, and physical pain. Description of each of these instigating conditions is valuable as each provides direction to specific intervention formulations. Treatment or management, in illustration, of self-injury motivated by escape from or avoidance of instructional demands may differ significantly from that provided escape-motivated self-injurious behaviors under the instigating conditions of physical pain or an intense state of dysphoria.

Specialized Assessments

Keep in mind that the purpose of assessment is to understand the "why" of challenging behaviors as a basis for devising individual centered interventions. Additional specialized psychological, medical, and/or psychiatric/neuropsychiatric evaluations thus may be needed in this assessment process if there is reason to suspect during the initial descriptive assessment that current conditions not adequately diagnosed are serving instigating, vulnerability, and/or reinforcing influences. As noted in the previous section, the initial clinical observations seek to lodge the behavior within physical, social, and program contexts. Additional specialized assessment may be indicated if:

- There are no apparent external environmental antecedents that account for the behavioral occurrences.

- Even if external antecedents are identified, there are obvious psychological, medical, or psychiatric conditions that produce symptoms that appear to coincide with or contribute to occurrence of the challenging behaviors.

- Challenging behaviors are accompanied by or correlated with such changes in the person's demeanor, mood, or physical signs as:

  - irritability,
  - grouchiness,
  - "looks glassy eyed,"
  - "does not seem to feel good,"
  - lower than usual frustration tolerance,
  - "flies off the handle more easily than usual,"
  - lower than usual energy level,
  - increase in usual activity level especially of a "jumpy" nature,
  - decease in time usually spent on tasks or preferred activities,
  - decrease in typical attention span and task focus.

- There is an increase in frequency, severity, or duration of challenging behavioral symptoms that persists for a few days or longer and appears to be independent of changes in the physical or social environments.

- Occurrence or changes in challenging behaviors appear to be cyclic in nature such as monthly, about every two or three months, etc.

During this specialized assessment process of identifying, and/or eliminating possible modality of influences on challenging behaviors, the presence of *obvious* symptoms of medical or psychiatric conditions that appear to be involved in producing the challenging behaviors would be evaluated initiated. If obvious biomedical symptoms are not present, the writers have found it useful and most cost effective to evaluate psychological influences initially. If, however, these do not account for the challenging behaviors, medical evaluation may be considered. After identifying or ruling out medical conditions, if questions remain about the challenging behaviors that appear to be related to possible psychiatric conditions, referral is then made for psychiatric evaluation.

On referral for specialized evaluations, specific questions about the challenging behaviors should be raised rather than merely referring the person for "a psychological, physical, or psychiatric evaluation." Illustrations of these questions include:

- "Noticed a change in mood state over the last several weeks during which Ms. Miller's aggressive outbursts have increased in frequency and severity. Are there any *psychological* (or *medical* if medical conditions are suspected and/or psychological contributors have been ruled out, or *psychiatric* if psychiatric conditions are suspected and/or if psychological and medical conditions have been ruled out) reasons for this mood state change? Please offer suggested interventions based on your assessment."

• "Within the last month, Ms. G. has appeared confused and then becomes extremely negativistic if prompted to complete her work tasks. This seems to coincide with the recent changes in seizure medication. Please give us your opinion about the possible medication effects and recommendations for medical intervention."

The more specific the questions asked of the specialist, the more useful the evaluation results will be in identifying potential instigating, vulnerability, and reinforcing conditions and in translating these into effective intervention approaches.

Step 3: Developing Diagnostic Formulations

As noted, integration of these specialized assessment data into the appropriate cells of the *Multimodal Contextual Behavior Analytic Worksheet* (Figure 1) provides the basis for completion of Column A (Diagnostic Hypotheses) of the Multimodal Integrated Intervention Plan (Figure 2). Numerous illustrations of these diagnostic hypotheses relating to possible instigating, vulnerability, and reinforcing influences were provided in Chapter Three. Completion of Column A insures integration of potential environmental, psychological, medical, and psychiatric "causes" into a cohesive diagnostic formulation plan.

Conclusion

We have spent a considerable amount of time in these initial

chapters discussing the "why" question that we began with—
What accounts for the challenging behaviors of persons with
developmental disabilities?

We discovered that there are a great many reasons why.

A large number of factors could influence both the challenging
and prosocial behaviors of any person on any one day. These
factors all have unique relationships to specific behaviors as well
as interacting with each other. This chapter has provided a format
for identifying and integrating these multiple factors. Chapter
Five provides guides for the important task of devising those
individual centered behavioral supports that hold promise of
improving the person's quality of life (Steps 4-9 of the Case
Formulation Process).

CHAPTER FIVE

CREATING PREVENTIVE AND PROACTIVE INTERVENTIONS

William I. Gardner

In previous chapters, we discussed possible causes of challenging behaviors in persons with developmental disabilities. We discovered that this is a complex issue, with many factors interacting to produce these behaviors in a way that is different for each individual. As noted, the Case Formulation Process of developing, implementing, and evaluating a set of *Individual Centered Behavioral Interventions* involves a number of sequential steps. Our focus now turns to Steps 4, 5, and 6 of this process. When completed, the resulting information translates into Column B (Program Objectives) and Column C (Diagnostically-based Interventions) of the Multimodal Integrated Intervention Plan. The chapter concludes with discussion of the remaining Columns of the Plan.

Case Formulation Process: Steps 4, 5, and 6

• Step 4: *Describing* program objectives specific to the "causes" identified in Step 3. *In some instances, these program objectives would involve specific socially and personally desirable alternative behaviors that represent functional equivalents, i.e., would satisfy the same personal need or motivation involved in the challenging behavior.* To illustrate, a person's aggressive behaviors may have become functional as these resulted in valued social attention. In this instance, the program objective would describe alternative appropriate ways of insuring that the person would obtain valued social attention.

In other instances, the program objective may directly address the motivational basis for the challenging behaviors. In this scenario, the motivation for the challenging behaviors would be viewed as abnormal in kind, intensity, frequency of occurrence, or duration of each occurrence. In illustration, Step 3 may suggest that a number of different events or conditions result in a high level of anger which, in turn, represents a major motivational state influencing occurrence of a range of verbal and physical aggressive behaviors. The related program objectives, in addition to describing alternative means of expressing anger, would address means of reducing or eliminating the excessive nature of the person's anger.

Finally, in some instances, the motivation for the challenging behaviors by its nature would be pathological. As illustrations, a person may gain enjoyment out of harming animals, setting fires, or having violent sexual contact with children. In other instances, a person's psychiatric features such as a dysphoric mood or delusional thoughts may provide the motivation for challenging behaviors. Program objectives would address the elimination of these pathological psychological and psychiatric features.

- Step 5: *Developing* a set of *intervention formulations* that address the current conditions hypothesized to influence the challenging behaviors.

- Step 6: *Selecting* an integrated set of *individual centered interventions* based on specific diagnostic-intervention formulations. To illustrate the difference between this step and Step 5, assume that assessment of a person's disruptive episodes results in a diagnostic hypothesis that this challenging behavior is being reinforced by the staff and peer attention that the behavior attracts. This diagnostic formulation translated in Step 5 to the logically related general intervention formulation "meet the person's need for attention as a means of removing the motivation for the challenging behavior." In Step 6, this general intervention strategy would next be translated into specific individual centered approaches such as, (a) minimize attention following disruptive behaviors, (b) provide social attention following prosocial behaviors, (c) provide frequent noncontingent positive social attention, (d) teach appropriate ways of soliciting attention, and (e) enrich the person's opportunities for positive social interactions with peers and staff.

Interventions resulting from Steps 5 and 6 would focus on:

- removing or minimizing biomedical and psychosocial influences presumed to instigate and reinforce the challenging behavioral symptoms,

- teaching prosocial skills as adaptive functional replacements for the challenging behaviors,

- increasing the person's motivation to use these newly acquired prosocial skills, and

- reducing or eliminating biomedical and psychological abnormalities and pathological socioenvironmental conditions that
  serve as vulnerability influences.

A skill enhancement focus is especially pertinent for persons with
mental retardation and mental health concerns who typically have
highly impoverished repertoires of coping behaviors. In this
personal context, challenging behaviors such as aggression or
excessive social withdrawal may represent highly effective and
efficient functional responses to aversive demands or conditions.
As such, these must be replaced by equally effective and efficient
functionally equivalent prosocial coping skills if the challenging
symptoms are to be minimized or eliminated.

As illustrated previously, some personal characteristics such as
social and coping skills, communication skills, motivational features, and personality characteristics, by their absence or low
strength, may increase the likelihood of challenging behaviors in
those persons inclined to use these responses to cope with external
or internal instigating conditions. No functionally equivalent
alternative behaviors may be present in the person's repertoire or,
if present, may not be as effective or efficient as the challenging
behaviors in meeting the person's current motivational features.
Thus, when developing intervention approaches for a person's
current challenging behaviors, knowledge of these vulnerability
conditions (deficit areas) guides the clinician in simultaneously
pinpointing the specific functionally equivalent coping skills and
related cognitive, emotional, and motivational supports needed
for continued successful social and interpersonal functioning
following termination of the behavioral supports program.

Other personal features of a biomedical and/or psychological
nature may be pathological in nature and also represent ongoing

risk or vulnerability influences. A partially controlled seizure disorder, a borderline personality disorder, a personality trait of suspiciousness, or constricted social motivational features may greatly increase the person's risk of engaging in impulsive violent outbursts when exposed to provoking events. Interventions are designed to address those vulnerability conditions specifically relevant to a person's challenging behaviors.

Treatment, Management, and Containment Procedures

When using diagnostic formulations as a basis for selecting interventions, distinctions are made between those biomedical and psychosocial interventions selected to produce *educative, training, or treatment* effects, (i.e., those selected to produce long-lasting changes in biomedical, behavioral, cognitive, emotional, and perceptual features of the person) and those selected to *manage* the challenging behavioral symptoms. Additionally, a distinction is made between these treatment and management procedures and other interventions used to *contain* specific episodes following their occurrence.

The primary focus of individual centered interventions should be that of proactive *treatment* and *proactive management* rather than *reactive management or containment* of challenging behavioral and emotional symptoms. Reactive management and containment of symptoms can be justified as a focus of intervention only after appropriate individualized diagnostic and treatment services of a biopsychosocial nature have been provided but found not to be successful in producing enduring changes in those psychological or psychiatric features presumed to be major determinants of these symptoms. The major objective of programming may then become one of identifying the best combination of medical, psychiatric, psychological, and socioenvironmental supports to insure adaptation to a community setting. This placement should be selected to accommodate the person's remaining vulnerabilities while utilizing his/her competencies as a means of minimizing recurrence of the challenging behavior symptoms.

Treatment Procedures

Active *treatment* refers to those biomedical and psychosocial interventions designed both:

- to reduce/eliminate the biomedical and psychosocial instigating and maintaining conditions that influence the frequency, duration, and intensity/severity of challenging behavioral symptoms, and

- to develop and/or strengthen psychosocial features that insure effective and efficient alternatives to the behavioral symptoms, e.g., expressing anger appropriately through verbal or other coping means.

In sum, the major objective of treatment interventions is that of producing enduring changes in the conditions that produce the challenging behavioral symptoms and of providing prosocial replacement skills that will persist across time and situations following termination of the treatment approaches.

These treatment interventions, to elaborate, are designed both:

- to remove external (e.g., abusive parental mode of interaction) or internal (e.g., hallucinations, dysphoric mood, chronic suspiciousness of the intent of others, anger) conditions that influence occurrence and persistence of target symptoms and/ or

- to change the person's responsiveness to those conditions that cannot be eliminated (e.g., teaching anger management skills).

Biomedical Treatment

Biomedical interventions may produce a *treatment* effect on challenging behavioral symptoms by removing/minimizing the instigating stimulus conditions associated with physical, bio-chemical, or neurological abnormalities and/or by eliminating or reducing biomedical conditions that represent vulnerabilities. To illustrate, neuroleptic medication during an active phase of a schizophrenic disorder may be used to reduce or eliminate such specific symptoms as hallucinations, delusions, and other cogni-tive/language abnormalities. Challenging behavioral symptoms such as aggression would also be reduced to the extent that these psychiatric symptoms are involved in influencing the aggressive episodes. If a treatment effect is realized (i.e., long-lasting elimination of these psychiatric symptoms), the medication could be removed without symptom recurrence. The person thus would be free of the psychiatric symptoms in the absence of the medication.

Psychosocial Treatment

Psychosocial interventions may produce a *treatment* effect if these either:

- result in the elimination of instigating and vulnerability con-ditions (e.g., reducing or eliminating excessive anger arousal through emotional retraining procedures), or

- effectively teach new skills that change the person's responses
  to these instigating conditions (e.g., teaching anger management skills as a means of effectively coping with excessive
  anger arousal as it occurs).

In selecting psychosocial therapy/teaching/training procedures, it
is critical that these procedures represent a suitable match with the
cognitive, emotional, and motivational features of person supported. A *cognitive therapy/teaching approach* when used with
persons with mental retardation and significant mental health
concerns in most instances is inappropriate for use as the major
teaching method for these persons.   A *direct skills therapy/
training approach,* in contrast, provides a better match between
training procedures and individual characteristics.   Each approach is described.

A *cognitive therapy/teaching approach* uses verbal interactions
and cognitive processing as its modality of delivering treatment
and training. Effectiveness is based on the assumption that if a
person acknowledges an understanding of a situation or gains an
understanding/insight into his/her problems, he/she then is able
to utilize that cognitive information to guide his/her behavior
under future *in situ* conditions. This assumes automatic generalization of cognitive knowledge gained from one time/situation to
another.   This approach involves use of cognitive activities
(discussions between client and staff; classroom instructions;
rules/expected behaviors presented in verbal or written form,
writing behaviors, thoughts, and feelings in a log/notebook for
further discussion and review with staff, verbal/insight-based
counseling and psychotherapy) as the major modes of therapy/
training.

This modality of therapy/teaching may be appropriate for verbally and cognitively skillful persons who are self-motivated to gain an understanding of the basis for their psychological symptoms (e.g., aggression, sexually abusive acts) and, once new insights or cognitive skills are gained, to use newly acquired cognitive strategies under future conditions of internal (e.g., anger, sexual arousal, anxiety) or external (e.g., provocative barbs from peers, reprimand from staff, rejection of sexual advances) stimulation to self-direct prosocial coping reactions. However, these assumptions are highly suspect when applied to persons with limited cognitive skills especially, as frequently is the case, if the person also presents central problems of impulse control.

A *skills therapy/training (habilitative) approach*, in contrast to the cognitive approach, is based on a concrete direct training approach. Specific adaptive skills relating to emotional, cognitive, and behavioral domains, selected on the basis of individual diagnostic formulations that can be used by that individual to cope with specific problem situations, are taught initially. Concrete (rather than abstract cognitive) representations of skill deficits are used to facilitate learning. Modeling, role playing, behavior rehearsal, specific performance feedback, self-monitoring, self-evaluation, self-consequation, and self-instruction along with eventual practice of skills *in situ* represent major therapy/teaching tactics. Situations in which problem behaviors occur are progressively reconstructed during training to insure functional utility for the person as these situations are faced in the future. Additionally, following success in specific situations, the person is then taught more general problem solving skills for use in other similar situations. Specific procedures, including cognitive labeling, self-talk, and problem solving skills, are used to train for generalization of these skills to future conditions. (Note the sequence: initially train specific coping skills, then teach the person to self-manage these when confronted with problem situations.)

This *skills training approach* is ideally suited for persons with limited cognitive skills as the person is taught specific skills rather than assuming that cognitive representations learned during verbal exchanges will be translated into action, as is done in the cognitive teaching approach. In the context of the skills training approach, the functional significance of any program component and its objective(s) can be evaluated relative to the program objectives established for each person.

Management Procedures

Management of challenging behavioral symptoms in a *proactive* manner *(i.e., doing something prior to the occurrence of the challenging behavior to minimize its occurrence)* refers to use of biomedical and psychosocial interventions that:

• eliminate or minimize triggering and contributing instigating conditions related to challenging behavioral symptoms, and/ or

• create or enhance instigating stimulus conditions that influence occurrence of prosocial behaviors that compete with challenging symptoms.

Management approaches of a *reactive nature* are used to minimize the duration and intensity of challenging behaviors after these do occur.

Neither proactive nor reactive management procedures actively teach alternatives coping skills or produce enduring symptom change. In fact, after termination of the management interventions, and on future exposure to the instigating conditions, the challenging behaviors are likely to recur as no long lasting changes in the "causes" of these have been produced.

Biomedical Management

Management of behavioral symptoms may result from biomedical interventions. In illustration, psychopharmacological intervention involving drugs such as lithium or carbamazepine may reduce a person's irritability or generalized restlessness, and aggressive responding that are influenced by these instigating conditions. On termination of the drug regimen, the person's irritability may return to the preintervention levels. The drug regimen thus serves to reduce the aggression by managing a component of the stimulus complex involved in its instigation. As the person's irritability level is not reduced or eliminated in an enduring manner after drug withdrawal, the person's inclination to aggression in the absence of the medication has not been reduced.

Psychosocial Management

Psychosocial management refers to those procedures selected to:

- eliminate or minimize specific stimulus conditions likely to instigate target symptoms,

- present or emphasize specific stimulus conditions that increase the likelihood of those prosocial behaviors most likely to compete with the challenging behaviors,

- present or emphasize specific stimulus conditions that inhibit the occurrence of challenging behaviors, and

- minimize the duration and intensity of challenging behaviors following their occurrence.

The initial three procedures are *proactive* in nature as these involve changing antecedents that *precede* challenging behavioral symptoms. These are designed to encourage alternative prosocial actions *currently available in the person's repertoire.* The fourth psychosocial management procedure is *reactive* in nature and initiated *following* the occurrence of problem behaviors. Even though reactive, this management procedure may prove quite valuable in minimizing the effects of any specific disruptive act. These management procedures as a group are supportive of active treatment efforts, but differ critically in function and effect as these are unlikely in isolation to produce durable changes in the conditions that result in challenging behavioral symptoms.

Proactive Psychosocial Procedures

In the first proactive approach, management procedures are initiated that serve to *remove or minimize* the effects of specific preceding conditions that instigate target symptoms. As examples,

A staff member who consistently provokes anger and negativism in persons attending a work training program may be reassigned. A person who easily becomes agitated when provided staff directives may be provided multiple choices, including the right of refusal. In these instances, the likelihood of becoming negativistic and agitated is reduced by controlling the stimulus conditions that provoke these behaviors. Note, however, that the person has not changed. Rather, the environment was modified to remove the instigating conditions—thus management rather than treatment.

In the second proactive management approach, stimulus conditions are *presented* that increase the likelihood of prosocial adaptive behaviors currently in the person's repertoire will replace the inappropriate action. As an example:

It has been shown that availability of strongly preferred reinforcers for following directives under aversive demand conditions results in an increase in a person's prosocial behaviors and a concomitant decrease in the previously observed aberrant behaviors. The reinforcers serve as a contributing instigating condition for prosocial behaviors that successfully compete with the challenging behaviors.

In the third proactive management procedure, inappropriate behaviors are inhibited by the presentation of conditions that signal the potential occurrence of negative consequences following a problem behavior.

In illustration, providing a reminder that occurrence of a specific aggressive behavior will result in loss of valued privileges may serve to inhibit the occurrence of the problem behavior.

Reactive Psychosocial Procedures

The final management procedure is used after inappropriate behavior has begun. This *reactive* procedure is designed to terminate or decrease the duration and/or intensity of the current episode.

> Such specific approaches as redirection, removing or reducing the instigating conditions, ignoring the behavior when acknowledging it would serve to intensify it, and removing the person from the source of instigation (e.g., removing the person to a quiet area away from the provoking noisy environment) illustrate the types of reactive tactics that may serve this management function

Psychosocial Management: Summary

As indicated, the primary objectives of management procedures is to facilitate or inhibit the occurrence of specific behaviors. To illustrate:

> A diagnostic assessment may reveal an increased likelihood of aggressive responding under conditions of specific task demands and reduced social attention. With this diagnostic information, the occurrence of disruptive behaviors may be reduced or even eliminated by removing these controlling conditions, that is, by never presenting task demands and/or by continually providing a rich

schedule of social attention. Whenever the controlling stimulus events of task demands and reduced social attention are reintroduced, however, the problem behavior could be expected to reappear. The strength of aggression in the presence of these controlling conditions has not been altered by the use of the management procedures. Durable changes could be expected only when treatment procedures are included that actively teach and insure durable alternative responses to these controlling events.

As a second illustration:

Assessment may reveal that a person's episodes of agitation and aggression could be minimized in intensity and duration if, immediately following initial signs of agitation, the person is redirected into alternative activities. The strength of these problem behaviors is not altered by this management procedure; rather their disruptive features are minimized. With consistent use of this management procedure, the person may quickly become available to participate in whatever treatment experiences are provided. This management program could be expanded by adding treatment components that, for example, would teach the person (a) to recognize his own early signs of agitation and then (b) to self-initiate alternative activities that would reduce or remove his agitation and the subsequent aggression.

Containment of Challenging Behaviors

Containment of challenging behaviors refers to use of biomedical and psychosocial interventions with out-of-control behaviors that pose a potential danger to the person and/or those in the environment. These containment procedures include the use of various *medications* (e.g., use of neuroleptic medication to stabilize a person's mood, mental status, or behavior) and *physical restraints* (e.g., physically holding the person). These procedures are used in emergency situations for the sole purpose of containing the individual for the duration of a current out-of-control crisis. These are used only after other treatment and management procedures have failed.

The purpose of behavior containment procedures is neither to produce durable behavior change nor to reduce the likelihood that a current behavior episode will escalate to out-of-control status (that is, to serve as a management procedure). Rather, behavior containment procedures are used to protect the person who has not responded to treatment or management procedures and already has reached an out-of-control status. His/her actions are restrained to minimize the possibility of injury to self or others.

It is, of course, possible that some behavior containment procedures for some individuals (e.g., isolating an out-of-control person or physically restraining a person's movement until behavior control is regained) may have a treatment effect (i.e., a reinforcing or punishing effect) of increasing, or reducing, the future likelihood of the out-of-control behavior. However, a particular containment procedure used with a specific person in neither selected nor used to produce this effect.

Interrelations of Procedures

As emphasized, intervention programs for challenging behaviors should have the dual objectives of teaching and/or strengthening the discriminated occurrence of personally satisfying and socially appropriate adaptive behaviors and of reducing or eliminating excessively occurring challenging behaviors. To accomplish these objectives, multimodal programs most frequently will include, in addition to treatment/training procedures designed to contribute to durable change:

*   those supportive biomedical and psychosocial management procedures designed to facilitate occurrence of desired behavior and to minimize occurrence of challenging behaviors, and

*   when needed for those persons inclined to demonstrate out-of-control behaviors, behavior containment components. With effective treatment procedures, however, these supportive management and containment components may be faded gradually as treatment goals are accomplished and as the person is able to adapt appropriately under the normal or usual conditions of his/her living, work, and leisure environments.

Case Formulation Process: Step 7

*   Step 7 : *Developing* a staging plan for providing the various interventions, i.e., deciding on what interventions should be implemented initially and the sequence or timing of the remaining interventions,

Following selection of the specific interventions to address the presumed biomedical and psychosocial "causes" of the challenging behaviors, a staging plan (when should the various interventions be provided and in what sequence should these be initiated) is devised (Column D of the Multimodal Integrated Intervention Plan). Additionally, predictions are made about the effects of various interventions (type, magnitude, and time involved). These expectations are included in Column E of the Multimodal Integrated Intervention Plan.

Staging decisions are based on consideration of (a) the presumed magnitude of influence of specific interventions, (b) the need to sequentially present interventions that build on each other (i.e., the extent to which the effects of any specific intervention is dependent on the effects of earlier interventions), (c) the desirability of determining the separate effects of different interventions, especially those that are intrusive or represent some risk to the physical or psychological well-being of the person, and (d) the projected time period in which a treatment effect should be realized. In order to evaluate the effects of specific interventions, it may be necessary to initiate only one intervention at any given time. After determining the effects of this intervention, it may be continued, deleted if found ineffective, or other interventions added to address other instigating, vulnerability, or maintaining influences.

Bambara, Mitchell-Kvacky, and Iacobelli (1994) describe a useful way of thinking about how to combine case formulation information to develop a treatment plan.

They look at treatment in terms of a time frame for planning when we will carry out our various interventions. The time frame is conceptualized in terms of short term interventions, intermediate interventions, and long term interventions.

Short-term interventions will have a relatively immediate impact on reducing the person's problem behavior. Such interventions include modifying the antecedents (what happens before the problem behavior occurs), applying different consequence strategies (using procedures which involve manipulating reinforcement), and if necessary, crisis management.

Intermediate interventions involves training alternative skills such as new prosocial behaviors that can replace the challenging behaviors along with general skills such as tolerance and coping. Presume that challenging behaviors revolve around chores in the group home. Interventions will have a longer term impact, for example, if the person has been provided choices regarding when he carries out chores and is taught to avoid some chores altogether by trading duties with others or paying someone else to carry out the chores.

Long term interventions focus on enhancing general competencies and lifestyle changes such as settings, activities, routines, and relationships.

Case Formulation Process: Step 8

•   Step 8: *Devising* and *implementing* procedures for evaluation of the effectiveness of interventions.

The next step in the Case Formulation Process involves deciding on the types of assessments needed to evaluate the effects of specific interventions. (Column F of the Multimodal Integrated Intervention Plan). These procedures may involve standardized scales and inventories but in most instances will require individually developed procedures. For example, a diagnostic hypothesis

that anxiety serves as a contributing condition for repeated episodes of agitated/disruptive outbursts may result in a related
intervention involving medication to reduce the anxiety. An
assessment procedure that specifically addresses changes in anxiety level is needed to evaluate the effects of this drug intervention.
It is possible that the drug therapy will produce reduction in
anxiety symptoms but have no effect on the frequency or severity
of agitated/disruptive episodes. In this scenario, it may be
concluded that the medication, while effective in treating anxiety,
is nonetheless ineffective in influencing the agitated episodes.
Other interventions derived from other diagnostic hypotheses
would be initiated.

Case Formulation Process: Step 9

*   Step 9: *Modifying* hunches (hypotheses) and/or interventions
    based on evaluation results.

The final step in the Case Formulation Process involves modification of hypotheses and related interventions based on evaluation of the effects of current interventions. Prior to discarding
hypotheses and related interventions, however, determination
should be made that the interventions have in fact been used on a
consistent basis. This involves specifying the staff responsible for
delivering and monitoring (data collection) along with devising a
schedule of reviewing the effects of each intervention (Column G,
Multimodal Integrated Intervention Plan). These procedures
reduce the likelihood that ineffective procedures will be continued beyond the intervention period previously designated (Column E, Multimodal Integrated Intervention Plan).

Conclusion

This chapter described the process of translating diagnostic formulations into related interventions. The remaining chapters provide more details on how to use the information obtained during the case formulation process to insure that interventions are indeed individual centered and focus primarily on improving the quality of life of those supported.

CHAPTER SIX

CREATING HABILITATIVELY APPROPRIATE ENVIRONMENTS

Dorothy M. Griffiths, William I. Gardner and Jo Anne Nugent

This Chapter describes another feature of the *Individual Centered Behavioral Interventions* approach. In previous chapters, we emphasized that aspects of the physical, social, and program environments may serve as instigating conditions for a person's challenging behaviors. In other instances, aspects of a person's environments may represent vulnerability conditions that place the person at increased risk for developing and using challenging behaviors. A number of writers have described the roles assumed by aberrant aspects of a person's environment in influencing the development of challenging behaviors in persons who are unable to cope with these conditions through use of more socially appropriate actions (Gardner, 1996; Martens & Witt, 1988).

Just as the environment can play a role in the development of inappropriate behavior, a more appropriate habilitative environment may contribute to prosocial behaviors. This habilitative environment provides stimulation, expectations, interactions and reinforcement, all which are therapeutic ingredients for development of competing prosocial behaviors and more general social development.

Following description of features of habilitatively appropriate
environments, suggestions are provided on how to created those
environmental conditions that promote positive lifestyles of persons with developmental disabilities.

Features of The Habilitatively Appropriate Environment

Let's begin by offering a definition of the habilitatively appropriate environment:

*A normalized environment that promotes learning and use of
those skills and behaviors that result in an enriched lifestyle for
the individual.*

The key elements of this definition are:

*   *normalized* — this term, based on the work of Wolfensberger
    (1972), suggests that the environment should be as typical as
    possible.

*   *promotes learning* — the habilitatively appropriate environ-
    ment is educative and provides supports and stimulation for
    the individual to learn prosocial alternatives to challenging
    behaviors.

*   *enriched lifestyle* — the ultimate purpose of a normalized
    evniroment is to support the person in experiencing a ful-
    filled quality of life.

*   *individual* — the lifestyle goals are uniquely defined by each
    person.

Environmental quality represents the key feature that adds to or interferes with the person's quality of life. Like all of us, persons with developmental disabilities benefit from high quality physical and social environments. Unfortunately, as we all know, persons with significant challenging behaviors often live in poor quality environments with unpleasant physical conditions, limited habilitatively appropriate programming, and sterile social conditions (Griffiths, 1998). We also know that poorly developed social, coping, and related skills combine with a range of biomedical conditions to render the person more vulnerable to the negative effects of such environments. It is not surprising that "problem" behaviors in persons with developmental disabilities frequently reflect negative environmental conditions.

Dimensions of Quality of Life

Evaluation of quality of life has been described along the three dimensions of *being, belonging,* and *becoming* (Renwick, Brown, & Raphael, 1994). This view suggests that quality of life is determined by a number of personal and social features, including:

*   having physical and psychological health and well being and a personal sense of meaning,

*   having a sense of belonging in one's environments, meaningful relationships, and access to one's community, and

*   engaging in everyday leisure and growth enhancing activities of life.

Renwick et al. (1994) suggest that each individual places different values on each of these. The value to the person is influenced heavily by the degree of personal control or choice over aspects of his/her live, access to opportunities available, and the relative enjoyment experienced in daily activities.

How does quality of life features influence the person's behavior? A case vignette provides illustrations of this relationship.

Paul was seventeen when moved from a large residential setting into a community group home. The written personal profile included such descriptions as "loves open spaces," "gains enjoyment from lengthy daily walks in the yard," and "is extremely active and needs a change of structured activities about every half hour." Recommendation for placement indicated that he "be in an area with independent access to a park" and that he "live with other young men who like active sporting events." Employment recommendations included "he be provided employment in a work setting that permitted him to move around and change activities often (e.g., shipping and receiving or even heavy cleaning jobs)."

Unfortunately, the community agency disregarded the recommendations and placed Paul in a group home with three men in their late 50's who had sedentary and quiet lifestyles. The group home was located in a busy area of the city, had no back yard for physical activities, and, due to the traffic pattern, did not permit Paul to go out safely without being accompanied by staff. Staff were quite comfortable with the routines of the house and were not willing to adapt the environment for Paul as they felt it would be disruptive to the other men in the home. Paul's work placement involved assembling a single item for the six hours of his work day.

The placement failed within the first few months as Paul showed increasing agitation, irritability, and finally, physical aggression. A behavior program had been developed to eliminate these behaviors but was unsuccessful as the reasons for the challenging behaviors were not addressed. The staff remarked that Paul should not have been referred for community placement as he did not have the skills to adjust to the new opportunities provided him.

In evaluating this placement failure, it is evident that the physical, social, and work environments offered minimal elements of quality for Paul. It did not provide the means for him to meet his needs for physical activity and a sense of independence. It did not welcome him as a unique person with a unique set of needs. In fact, Paul's uniqueness was ignored through staff expectations that he establish relationships with individuals with whom he shared few if any common interests. Simultaneously, the placement denied him access to community events and resources. On all levels of being, belonging, and becoming, this new placement was lacking in quality for Paul. Paul reacted in the only way he knew. He vented his frustrations through challenging behaviors. These eventually were successful in his escaping from a lifestyle that did not attend to his uniqueness as a person.

Ultimately, the habilitatively appropriate environment is defined by the outcomes that result from exposure to it. Outcome is measured by the appropriateness of the environment for an individual. We evaluate how the individual responds to the environment and how well the environment facilitates the person's positive adaptation.

Notice how this perspective turns the typical concept of challenging behavior problems upside down. Rather than placing the blame for challenging behaviors on the person, we examine the role of features of the environment in contributing to the occurrence and severity of the behaviors. With this perspective, environmental changes represent a major focus of our interventions rather than one that seeks to change the person to fit the requirements of inappropriate residential, social, and work environments.

Why Establish Habilitatively Appropriate Environments?

The habilitatively appropriate environment is more than a place in which an individual's basic care needs are met. It is assumed that each person has the right to a warm shelter, food, clothing, and freedom from abuse. The habilitatively appropriate environment in addition provides the person with the opportunities, supports, and interactions to ensure that he/she is able to achieve a quality of life suitable to his/her needs and aspirations.

The following discussion considers the roles that the person's environments play in the initial development and persistent recurrence of challenging behaviors. The person's environments may contribute to challenging behaviors in two ways. First, different environments such as the place of residence or the work setting may contain specific instigating conditions (both triggering and/ or contributing), vulnerabilities, and reinforcing consequences for problem behaviors. Second, as the habilitatively appropriate environment represents an important component in treatment and management efforts, an enviornment that is not supportive of an individual centered perspective would be detrimental to habilitative endeavors.

Environmental Conditions as Instigating Influences

One of the initial questions posed when seeking to understand challenging behaviors is whether specific changes in the person's environment would result in reduction or elimination of the challenging behaviors.

It is easy to understand why persons who live in environments that are overcrowded, lacking in privacy, unstimulating, lacking in positive interactions, and in some case, even physically or psychologically abusive, may develop challenging behaviors as attempts to cope with these conditions. In most setting, however, it is not these obvious conditions that influence development and persistent recurrence of these behaviors. Rather, conditions more specific to the unique needs of a person may represent significant instigating influences.

The presence or absence of certain environmental events or conditions has been shown to influence some challenging behaviors. These include the availability of reinforcers and the associated contingencies, specific staff members present in a group home, work requirements, changes in the frequency and quality of social attention, space, type of activities, materials, and presence of specific peers (Gardner et al., 1986).

Experience with Mr. Thomas Charles, living in a multi-bed group home with 14 other adults, represents an example of this relation between specific features of the environment and the unique needs of a person.

When observing Thomas in this residential environment, it became evident that his challenging behaviors occurred when too many people were around, noise level was excessive, and whenever excessive demands were made. These represented conditions that were likely to be present during mealtimes in his group home. When these conditions were present, Thomas would become emotionally distressed and likely to engage in aggression (Griffiths, Richards, & Fedoroff, 1998).

In this case, management approaches of reducing these instigating environmental conditions resulted in a reduction of the challenging behaviors. Attempting to change the challenging behaviors initially without addressing these critical environmental conditions would have been unsuccessful. If interventions of an intrusive or punitive nature were used, it is possible that a short-term reduction in the behaviors would have resulted. However, positive long term results would only occur if we address the environmental factors and the manner that these interact with some of Thomas's personal features.

A further rapid reduction in frequency and severity of Thomas's challenging behaviors followed his move to a living environment in which the instigating conditions were seldom present. He was moved to an environment with fewer people, less noise, fewer demands, and a predictable daily routine. Even though the challenging behaviors did not completely disappear, these did became infrequent following these critical changes in his living environment. Thomas had other problems that required attention, including a number of medical concerns. Thus, environmental conditions in most instances are not the only "causes" of problem behaviors but, as illustrated, may serve as significant instigating influences in producing these.

Environments Supportive of Habilitation

Experience with Jane illustrates this support:

Jane, a 12-year-old girl, was engaging in aggressive outbursts in school. These behaviors did not occur in the home setting. Observation of her in both settings revealed that Jane's mother had learned to understand Jane's subtle and personal communication methods. When Jane wanted to be move, have a change in activities, or when she was hungry, she communicated this to her mother with subtle sound and motor actions. While at school, the teachers were neither aware of this communication style nor had the time to observe as attentively as Jane's mother. Consequently, Jane's lack of a universal communication strategy represent a *vulnerability that increased the risk of problem behaviors* in any environment where mother was not present to detect and respond to her needs.

With this information, the teachers began to learn Jane's communication style. Even if successful, however, Jane's current method of communicating her needs and desires when with other people or new environments would leave her vulnerable or at high risk to use the challenging behaviors in response to her undetected communication attempts and unmet needs. The teachers began to introduce Jane to an alternative communication system that gradually would replace her current style. The new method was one that could be more widely understood by various persons in a variety of settings, thereby reducing the need for challenging behaviors.

This example illustrates that the habilitatively appropriate environment is one that recognizes a person's *vulnerabilities* and provides experiences designed to teach alternative methods of coping with the events that instigate problem behaviors. As a second example:

Mr. Irv Williams is extremely sensitive to changes in his daily routine and expresses his distress with loud verbal outbursts. An habilitatively appropriate environment would provide a routine, predictable, and organized life space for him. At the same time, efforts would be made to teach Mr. Williams more appropriate coping skills for use when changes do occur.

In some instances, changes or adaptations in the environment may be temporary in nature as the person learns new adaptive skills of responding more appropriately to the original instigating conditions. In other cases, a person may be unable to learn alternative coping strategies. As a result, an habilitatively appropriate environment would adapt to the characteristics of the person. As an example:

Mr. Peter Grimes, a young man with a traumatic brain injury, is highly vulnerable to engage in increased levels of agitation in response to loud noises. If these noises are not removed, he engages in severe self-injury. Although Peter has learned alternative means of coping with unexpected noise (e.g., to leave the location when appropriate), his routines have been adapted to avoid noisy places whenever possible. For example, he avoids malls or only goes at times during which few people and activities are likely to be present.

In this example, it was not possible to change Peter's vulnerability (i.e., his brain injury and the resulting tendency to be easily overaroused). It was possible to provide alternative ways to avoid those conditions that resulted in the overarousal and self-injury.

Habilitatively Appropriate Physical Environments

A number of elements of the physical environment contribute to the quality of an *habilitatively appropriate environment.* Each is described.

Proper Conditions

All people should live in conditions which are safe, clean, comfortable, and free from noxious sensory elements. As noted, numerous elements of the physical environment can serve as *instigating conditions* for challenging behavior. Not only should the environment be free of these conditions whenever possible, it also should include numerous instigating conditions for prosocial behaviors.

An environment that insures safety is crucial. People who are worried about their physical safety have little time for learning new skills. The stress can lead to many behavioral issues. For example, the impact of abuse can be devastating. One outcome could indeed be serious emotional symptoms (Nugent, 1994).

Clustering

In providing services for persons with developmental disabilities, it continues to be rather common to cluster individuals who have similar disabling conditions such as communication problems, hearing impairments, or behavioral challenges. Negative features have been noted in environments where people are clustered (Griffiths, 1998). Typically, clustered environments offer reduced opportunities for meeting a person's unique needs. First, these environments are not normative. Second, such environments require systemic and staffing patterns that may impede the development of appropriate skills, while increasing the probability of negative behaviors. Third, there is reduced opportunity for exposure to social models of appropriate behavior.

In view of these negative features, clustering produces a number of philosophic and clinical concerns that impede development of an habilitatively appropriate physical environment.

Space and Size

Social density, crowding, and the resultant lack of privacy have been found to correlate with problem behavior (Griffiths, 1986). Social density refers not just to space but also to the number of people using the space and the use made of it. Privacy is important to all human beings, particularly with respect to activities such as hygiene, eating, sleeping, and sexual expression.

Normative

In our definition of the *habilitatively appropriate environment,* we included the concept of normative. This is based on the writings of Wolfensberger on normalization (Wolfensberger, 1972). Normalization implies that culturally normal means are used to establish or maintain behaviors that are as culturally normative as possible.

Providing normative physical environments promote generalization. Generalization means that something is made universally applicable. With reference to behavior, it means that the same or similar behaviors are appropriate when used in different environments.

Persons with developmental disabilities have difficulties with generalization. They may learn a skill in one environment and not apply it in another. For example, a person with a developmental disability may know how to take the same bus every day from his group home to work and return. However, he may not be able to use any other bus routes since the skills associated with taking a bus have not generalized.

What does this have to do with normalization? The probability of generalization is increased if environments are similar in key elements. If someone lives in a home environment that is quite typical, he/she will be likely to use the skills learned in that home environment in other homes. If, on the other hand, someone learns a skill in an institutional-like environment, he/she is not as likely to use that skill in a typical home enviroment. The two environments are not similar enough for generalization to occur.

To illustrate this point, a proper work environment is needed to teach proper work habits. It will be difficult to convince someone that attendance, punctuality, and work clothes are necessary if the work environment is more school or recreational in nature. An inappropriate work environment would have a direct impact on challenging behavior which in turn impede the learning of work habits.

In sum, normalization is a desired feature of all environments for persons with developmental disabilities. Normalization of environments is a broad concept, including physical elements, routines, and experiences.

Opportunities for Stimulation and Learning

Since persons with developmental disabilities have learning difficulties, we want to maximize the probability of their learning. One way of doing this is to provide variety and stimulation in their environments. This increases the person's attention and interest in the task at hand.

A person should be in the appropriate and normative environment for each activity of the day. Activities should not be restricted to the person's home. Some recreation should take place in recreational locations such as health clubs or movie theaters; employment should occur in normalized job settings. Variety and stimulation make life in general much more enjoyable!

Habilitatively Appropriate Social Environments

Characteristics of *habilitatively appropriate social environments* for persons with developmental disabilities include a number of features. Each is discussed.

Positive Relationships

People frequently indicate that what makes life worth living is the other people in their lives. People with developmental disabilities wish to have positive meaningful relationships just as we all do.

Positive relationships for a person with a developmental disability would include:

- a variety of relationships—acquaintances, friends, and loved ones,

- people who are part of the person's life because they wish to spend time with the person, not because they are paid to be there,

- the right to choose the people who are close—friends, lovers, spouses, roommates,

- privacy to develop close relationships without staff, other residents, or family always being present,

- the opportunity to demonstrate reciprocity—to be an equal partner in a relationship rather than always being the recipient of time, money, gifts, skills and support provided by others,

- minimal social isolation, except by choice, and

- the right to express personal sexual preferences in private.

These are all elements that any one of us wish and expect in our lives. Unfortunately, this is not often the case with persons with developmental disabilities. The absence of some of these may indeed contribute to occurrence of challenging behaviors.

The element of choice relative to living arrangements and house mates may be particularly significant in understanding challenging behaviors. The following experience with Ms. Dawn Belar illustrates this.

Ms. Belar, a middle aged woman, was moved to a group home with four other females in their mid teens. Dawn was quite unhappy with this arrangement. She developed extremely negative feelings toward one of the teens and disliked the energetic, noisy, adolescent lifestyle of her other housemates. Dawn's emotional distress over the living conditions became a major instigating influence for tantrums, disruptions, and eventual fights with the teen whom she found most distasteful. Numerous counseling sessions were held to offer alternative means of expressing her feelings and interpersonal conflicts. Additionally, a variety of reinforcement programs were offered. These were not effective in eliminating her challenging behaviors as her emotional turmoil was not resolved. Dawn persisted in reporting that she did not want to live with her house mates. Finally, after matters deteriorated to the point that the house was in constant turmoil, the agency moved Dawn into an apartment of her own.

Some staff were quite angry about this, insisting that the agency had "given in" to Dawn and reinforced her bad behavior. Yet, her challenging behaviors and unhappiness resulted from a highly unpleasant social environment and her lack of control over this critical aspect of her life.

If we think of ourselves, we would not want to live permanently in a home with four house mates toward whom we had extremely negative feelings for one and a distinct dislike for the other three. (We would probably not be living with four other people to begin with!) Yet this was happening to Dawn and she was being blamed for "acting out." Assessing this situation, we can see that the four housemates were sources of emotional distress that served a significant *instigating* influence over the problem behaviors. Her challenging behaviors reflected her frustration and displeasure. The *habilitatively appropriate social environment* would have respected her decisions, and promoted positive behavior by offering alternative living arrangements.

Stability

Another key element of *habilitatively appropriate social environments* is that of stability. Most of us like to spend our time with people we know. This is comforting and rewarding for us. It also provides the opportunity for more personal and intimate relationships to develop. We usually add new people to our lives while having the security of longer term relationships such as friends and family.

Unfortunately, people with developmental disabilities often experience a lack of stability in their social and interpersonal environments. They may be removed from family and friends to live in a completely different residential setting. Movement from residential setting to residential setting without choice often occurs. Staff and volunteers may come and go with no input from the person with developmental disabilities.

This lack of stability makes it very difficult for people to form meaningful relationships. This lack of stability can produce emotional distress that may in turn serve as an instigating influence for challenging behaviors. Probably most of us know of individuals who present problem behavior when a favorite staff member leaves. We can understand this from two perspectives— the disappearance of the person is emotionally distressful. This distress may serve as an instigating condition for problem behaviors. Additionally, under this condition of distress, the problem behaviors may produce personal attention that on a temporary basis may meet the emotional needs of sadness, worry, or feeling of abandonment. As a result of these reinforcing experiences, the challenging behaviors may become more frequent.

One way to deal with the distress associated with inevitable changes in staff is to encourage relationships with a number of people in a person's life, particularly people who will be more permanent. Also, more personal support can be provided during transitions. Both of these strategies contribute to the development of *habilitatively appropriate social environments*.

Community Involvement

As part of a normative lifestyle, it is crucial that people with developmental disabilities become part of the community. Their social environments should include opportunities for the full variety of interactions in a variety of locations. This community involvement provides excellent opportunities to meet people with shared interests who can offer sources of friendship. Community involvement also promotes the development of positive skills and a more fulfilling lifestyle.

Relationships With Staff

One major component of the social environments of most people with developmental disabilities is the staff who support them. It has long been acknowledged that the relationship between professionals and individuals to whom support is provided represents a component of successful clinical interventions (Rogers, 1973). The quality of interactions between staff and the person supported plays a central role in the *habilitatively appropriate environment.*

Habilitatively appropriate staff are those who see beyond the person's developmental disability and challenging behaviors and relate on a person-person basis. This staff believe in the importance of dealing with persons with developmental disabilities as people first. This involves showing an interest in the individual and having genuine concern about the person. Habilitatively appropriate staff are those who offer significant amounts of positive reinforcement and personal regard on an ongoing basis. In contrast, staff who do not demonstrate positive regard and respect will not be liked. Why would individuals want to learn skills from staff they don't like? Why would individuals care about receiving "positive" reinforcement from them? On the other hand, it is not advisable for staff to become so enmeshed with the individual that professional objectivity cannot be maintained. The appropriate role combines genuine warmth and concern with appreciation of the need for professional distance.

Some of the basic qualities of the *habilitatively appropriate social environment* summarized by Griffiths (1998) include:

• an adequate staffing ratio based on the needs of the individuals,

• physical integration of staff and residents during activities and routines such as meals and leisure time,

• a positive interactional atmosphere, with a high level of positive reinforcement, particularly relative to the amount of corrective feedback or discipline, and

• staff who spend the majority of their time interacting with individuals rather than carrying out administrative or housekeeping duties.

In sum, it is important to ensure that staffing patterns and duties are designed to develop *habilitatively appropriate environments*. Just as important is the expectation that staff will have respectful and supportive interactions with all individuals they support.

Structuring The Habilitatively Appropriate Program

Experiences with persons with developmental disabilities who present challenging behavioral and emotional expression emphasize the value of a well defined and structured habilitation environment. In this environment the person is best able to effectively and efficiently acquire social and coping skills along with those of self-management and self-responsibility. Under structured teaching and interpersonal conditions, the person is gradually provided increased responsibility for his/her own actions. If granted excessive initial independence in managing one's own behaviors, without acquiring the needed motivational/emotional and self-directing skills, the person is likely to experience excessive failure.

Establish Expectations

Much of our daily behavior is rule governed. We do not hit because we have learned that hitting is wrong. We take a bath because we have learned that there is an expectation of cleanliness. The list goes on. These basic rules of daily living have been internalized for most people as a result of explicit rules that were reinforced and the violations of which resulted in some social sanction, such as our mother's look or scolding. Over time these externalized expectations became routines that we complete because failure to do so would violate our own internalized expectations.

Using this very natural model, a therapeutic habilitative program must foster the development of rule governed behavior. This is achieved by establishing clear, explicit and consistent expectations for basic human interactions and daily living.

Well defined and explicitly represented standards of conduct are critical features of the habilitation environment. These standards function as guides for appropriate action. For individuals with behavioral and emotional challenges, the standards too often are ill-defined and inconsistently represented. When expectations are unclear, the person responds to whatever impulse or stimulation is present at the moment, often with inadequate concern over the appropriateness of the behavior or the immediate or long-term consequences that may result.

Expectations should be conveyed in a pleasant but matter-of-fact manner. Those behaviors that are appropriate and expected in various specific situations, such as meal times, in the bathroom, while watching television and the like, are set out as standards against which the person will learn to evaluate the appropriateness or inappropriateness of his or her own behaviors in these varying environmental settings.

Well defined behavioral expectations are needed also to ensure that all program staff consistently represent these in an informative and routine manner in both structured and informal interaction with each person being supported. With these consistent structured behavioral standards, each support staff has a common basis for relating to both appropriate and inappropriate behaviors. Finally, with more consistency in what is expected and how the social environment will relate to various behaviors, a potential source of confusion and conflict is removed. Each person soon begins to use his/her personal resources for constructive activities instead of "testing the limits" excessively as is frequently observed when inconsistent expectations are present.

Specify Contingencies

Establishing expectations is only half of the equation. The expectations must be paired with contingencies. The person is informed that there are specific consequences associated with what he or she may choose to do. Developing this "contingency sensitivity" represents the initial step in learning to be responsible for one's own behavior. In this way the person begins to take personal ownership for one's own behavior.

When individuals meet the expectations, there should be reinforcement (in the form of praise, recognition and perhaps more tangible items if needed) sufficient to establish the behavior as a routine. Moreover, social sanctions should result when the expectations are violated. It may be in the form of social reprimands, e.g., "John you have hurt Mary, you know that we do not hit in this house" or loss of privileges, e.g., "You have not bathed this week and therefore you have chosen not to go with us to the restaurant."

More specifically, in fostering contingency sensitivity, the person is informed of the behavior-consequence relationships, e.g., "Susan, you make me so happy when you dress yourself." "Steve you finished your work. Now you have some free time to do whatever you would like." "Lynn, remember after you finish your work we can go shopping for your new shoes." "Mike, remember our rule, if you fight with Carole over the TV, you have decided to lose the use of the TV for the rest of the day." Next the person is taught to label or demonstrate the behavior-consequence relationship, e.g., "Jill, what happens when you finish your work?" "Tom, when you yell at your friend, what happens?"

The positive and negative consequences involved in teaching contingency sensitivity and personal responsibility or ownership should reflect naturally occurring events whenever possible. In view of the motivational characteristics of persons with chronic behavioral challenges, naturally occurring consequences such as creating disappointment or distress in peers, family or staff may have only minimal influence on the person's behavior. As a result, other consequences, such as loss of privileges, restrictions of preferred activities, or delay in receiving desired reinforcers may be necessary. If the consequences are to be effective, they must be meaningful to the individual. To emphasize, events following desired behaviors should be positive or enjoyable to the person just as those following challenging behaviors should result in some personal discomfort or unpleasantness. In the absence, of this contrast, the person has no basis for developing skills of exercising personal choice in selecting which of his/her own behaviors will occur under varying conditions or to inhibit those in conflict with internalized standards of conduct.

In this habilitatively appropriate environment:

- If a person engages in inappropriate behavior of a minor nature, it is ignored whenever possible and the person is guided into a desired behavior.

- If a person is disruptive and persistently intrudes into the privacy of others, he/she is prompted to terminate his inappropriate behavior. If the behavior continues, the person is prompted to remove him/herself to an alternate location until control is regained.

- After self-control is evident, the person is encouraged to rejoin the activity and prompted to engage in alternative socially appropriate behaviors that result in positive consequences.

- If these are unsuccessful and the person continues to intrude into the privacy of others, more direct assistance is provided until the person can again assume responsibility for his/her behaviors.

Within the habilitation environment, consequences for challenging behavior are not impulsively imposed by staff. The person is aware of the consequences of various actions prior to the occurrence and encouraged to self-select those behaviors resulting in positive consequences. If the person chooses to act inappropriately, the person is informed that his or her own behaviors produce the contingent negative consequences.

Within the habilitatively appropriate environment, the individual becomes aware of and sensitized to contingencies, both positive and negative. In this manner, the person can be taught ownership, accountability and personal choice regarding one's behavior. It is important to remember, however, that unless the person has the necessary skills to engage in the desired behavior or has knowledge of the alternatives, there is no choice. Under these circumstances, the program focus should shift to one of teaching the prosocial skills.

To summarize, most inappropriate behaviors are reactive in nature. The person is reacting to either some internal impulse or some external provocation. Unless a person has learned standards of conduct or inhibitory controls, he/she may respond impulsively and without concern or awareness of the immediate or delayed effects of the behavior on him/herself and others. It is therefore important to structure the habilitation environment to teach both cognitive and affective awareness of and sensitivity to the relationship between a person's behavior and its various effects. In this manner the person develops a more generalized *contingency sensitivity*.

Realistic and consistent contingencies emphasize to the person that behaviors, whether appropriate or inappropriate, have specific personal as well as interpersonal effects and that he/she can influence these effects. This awareness and self-selection can be developed even by persons with severe developmental disabilities if provided consistent experiences within the structure of the habilitative environment.

Strengthen Social Motivation

The primary motivational objective of the habilitation environment is to increase the natural sources of motivation for prosocial behavior. As stated earlier, some individuals with challenging behaviors are not motivated by the impact they are having on others or the environment. To offset these motivational differences:

•   The habilitation environment should provide exposure to a variety of developmentally and socially appropriate incentives in order to teach the person to value these natural sources of motivation.

•   The habilitation program should emphasize development of meaningful personal relationships and the resulting social motivation that comes from such relationships.

•   The person should be taught to value his or her own accomplishments and to choose those ways of behaving, thinking and feeling that are self-enhancing.

Decrease Aversive Conditions

A second motivational objective of the habilitation program is to decrease the number of events that are aversive to the individual. Persons who present challenging behaviors often are unmotivated, uncooperative and disinterested in certain activities because they find these unpleasant. As discussed in previous chapters, most challenging behaviors result in escape and avoidance of situations that the person finds unpleasant, uncomfortable, or undesirable. In the habilitation environment, challenging behaviors can be reduced by systematic elimination or reduction of this aversiveness. The more naturally occurring of these may be reintroduced gradually once the person has a means of coping with these situations. By removing the aversive events until the individual has a means of gaining positive feedback for appropriate social behavior, social motivation is increased.

Provide Choices

As noted earlier, one key element of a desired quality of life is to have personal determination over ones own lifestyle. This includes having choice over such life conditions as where we live, with whom we live, where we work, our recreational pursuits, our sexual lifestyle, and our friends and acquaintances.

Of course, none of us has complete control over these or similar aspects of ones lifestyle. However, we still have considerable control over what happens to us on a day to day basis. As long as we stay within legal boundaries, we can pursue relatively personalized lifestyles. However, the same cannot be said for most persons with developmental disabilities who live within supervised programs.

Why does personal choice matter? An individual's challenging behaviors may be serving the *function* of telling others that he/she is unhappy about something in the environment that he/she would change if in possession of the freedom to do so. Unfortunately, persons with developmental disabilities frequently do not have the resources, the skills, and the power to make such changes.

They are usually without meaningful choice over their own environments. Therefore, challenging behaviors may be influenced by the personal distress resulting from a lack of control over meaningful aspects of the person's life.

Consider an example from the experience of one of the authors:

Mr. James Bandy, a 67-year-old man, lives in a group home with others who are considerable younger. He had always been a pleasant and cooperative man who enjoyed his lifestyle. At age 66, he began to protest going to work at a workshop. He stated that he wanted to retire. Unfortunately, as the agency was not able to provide staff in the group home during the day, it was necessary that Mr. Bandy go to the workshop to insure adequate supervision. Mr. Bandy became increasingly vocal about his desire to retire and began refusing to get ready for work in the morning. This caused considerable difficulty for the staff who had responsibility of getting others up and out the door on time during the work week. James became increasingly angry about going to work and began pushing staff away whenever they attempted to assist him in preparation for his work schedule.

Staff naturally became concerned about his aggressive actions. A behavior program was initiated in which he lost valued privileges such as phone calls to his family and cigarettes if he did not cooperate in the morning. This resulted in increased anger and aggression. These outbursts led to even further restriction of such activities as community outings.

A behavior consultant with an individual centered philosophy was enlisted. The following observations were offered:

- There were concerns about the man's human rights since privilege restriction was infringing on basic rights such as freedom to communicate with family,

- His request to retire was quite reasonable and normalized, and

- All attempts at behavior programming similar to the procedures used would be doomed to failure until the basic cause of the aggressive behavior, the distress created by the requirement that he continue work past retirement age, is addressed.

The agency accepted the consultant's report and agreed to deal with the request for retirement. Mr. Bandy was taught basic safety skills so that he could remain in his home without staff being present for reasonable periods of time during the day. A neighbor was enlisted to be a friendly support that could be contacted if immediate assistance was needed. Staff came by at noon to assist as needed with lunch preparation. Also, Mr. Bandy became involved in a local senior's center and spent several hours a week there engaging in leisure activities of his choice. His behavior problems disappeared.

This example illustrates how the lack of personal determination over valued aspects of a person's life can assume a major role in producing challenging behaviors. The intrusive interventions could not be effective because the central contributing condition was not addressed. Agencies exert considerable power over the lives of persons with developmental disabilities and administrative need sometimes supercedes individual need. On a brighter note, once the agency agreed to change, the team became quite creative and successful.

Enhance Self-Esteem

In addition to teaching a range of personal and social competency behaviors, the habilitation approach places a major emphasis on influencing a person's positive emotional and motivational development and expression. This is accomplished by providing a number of positive experiences and by relating these when possible to the person's day to day actions and other personal features.

Often persons with challenging behavior self-label in devaluing or degrading ways (e.g., bad, ugly, dumb, slow). In the habilitative environment, persons are taught to use alternative positive self-statements based on positive social roles that they assume. For example:

Mr. Steve Priest typically used devaluing phrases to describe himself at work. The staff decided to encourage him to learn to value his role as an adult worker. He was taught to self-label "I am a good adult worker. I finished all of my work. I'm proud of myself. I earned my money. I can buy something with what I earned." The emphasis was placed on Mr. Priest's competency and on the relationship between his behaviors and the resulting positive consequences.

As a second example:

> *After Jon Schmidt was observed helping a peer who was having difficulty, the supervisor remarked "Jon, I'm very pleased that you decided to help Susan. What a thoughtful person you are. I'll bet you really feel good about that." And later, "John tell me how it makes you feel when you help your friends." Additionally, the supervisor may comment to someone else, so that Jon can hear, about how thoughtful it was for Jon to help Susan.*

Enhance Self-Awareness

Habilitative environments also provide opportunity for individuals to learn to recognize, label and express negative emotions in an appropriate way. Anger, disappointment, jealously, frustration...represent negative emotions commonly experienced by most of us. Inappropriate behaviors of persons with developmental disabilities often result from the absence of appropriate means to cope with these negative emotions. The person may not have the skills to cope successfully with these typical stressors, and thus may behave in an overly emotional, disorganized, and disruptive manner.

In illustration:

> *Mr. Steve Bauer, an adult with mild developmental disabilities, becomes aggressive towards others when angry. Initially, it may be suggested "Steve, I know you are angry. But let's talk about it instead of hitting your friends."*

Or,

> *Paula Jean is an adolescent with moderate developmental disabilities. When Paula becomes upset with a peer, it might be said, "Paula, let's walk away and relax" as she is guided away from the source of provocation and prompted to breathe slowly and deeply.*

The habilitative environment supports a person in identifying, labeling, and responding appropriately to negative emotions. The means of coping with negative emotional arousal is followed by positive feedback.

Conclusion

We have discussed the impact on behavior of various features of both physical and social environments. It is clear that the general environments in which persons with developmental disabilities live cannot be ignored. Too often, we are led to believe that these environments cannot be changed because of such considerations as administrative needs and funding concerns. However, ethical concerns arise when an individual is experiencing challenging behavior and that behavior can be linked to aspects of the environment that potentially could be modified.

Is it ethically appropriate to attempt to change the individual to fit into an environment that is not meeting the person's needs? Or is it more ethically appropriate to change aspects of the environment to meet the needs of the individual? The latter is consistent with the *Individual Centered Behavior Interventions* approach advocated by the authors.

Quality behavioral supports involve *habilitatively appropriate environments* for people with developmental disabilities. Otherwise, many of our efforts will not be effective. We cannot expect positive behaviors and skill acquisition from people who live in environments that (a) contribute significantly to the *instigation* of challenging behavior, (b) do not recognize and proactively respond to the *vulnerabilities* of the individual, or (c) do not provide a positive atmosphere in which the person can learn appropriate alternatives to challenging behaviors.

CHAPTER SEVEN

PROACTIVE STRATEGIES FOR MANAGEMENT OF CHALLENGING BEHAVIORS

Dorothy M. Griffiths and Jo Anne Nugent

In Chapter Six, discussion focused on the possible role of features of the physical and social environments in instigating challenging behaviors. This chapter provides more detailed discussion of various strategies to use in modifying *instigating* influences by combining proactive behavior management with educative approaches to reduce or eliminate challenging behaviors.

In the past, challenging behaviors frequently were dealt with through using a variety of punishment strategies such as time out, overcorrection, response cost, and restraints (Gardner et al., 1986). Although these approaches have demonstrated effectiveness in reducing some problem behaviors, use of these procedures have been questioned for philosophical, legal, ethical, administrative and pragmatic reasons (Gardner et al., 1986, Gardner & Cole, 1986).

Other studies have suggested that an alternative to use of such negative consequence is to focus on the preceding conditions or *instigating* factors associated with the behavior (Gardner et al.,

1986). For example, one study demonstrated a decrease in challenging behaviors by changing or removing the antecedent instigating conditions (Touchette, MacDonald, & Langer, 1985). This and similar studies support the possibility that identification of the *instigating* events that produce challenging behaviors offers the possibility of reducing or eliminating these problem behaviors by the proactive management procedure of changing or removing these antecedents. Changes in antecedent events may result in an immediate change in challenging behaviors and, at the same time, provide time for teaching the person new skills to cope with these events when encountered in the future.

The procedure of changing antecedents is used not only to reduce the likelihood of challenging behavior but also to create conditions that influence occurrence of appropriate behavior. Recall the earlier discussion in Chapter Five of use of *proactive behavior management*. This procedure is discussed by Bambara et al., (1994), Gardner and Cole (1993), and Touchette and associates (1985) who report that removal of the antecedents for challenging behaviors and simultaneously replacing these with instigating conditions associated with prosocial behaviors may produce reduction or elimination of problem behaviors.

In summary, antecedent changes can be used both to reduce challenging behavior and to increase desired behavior or to create a structure for enhanced teaching to occur.

Gardner et al., (1986) have suggested that the knowledge of *instigating* conditions for challenging behaviors may suggest interventions that:

- *remove* or *reduce* the contributing instigating events for challenging behaviors, e.g., Staff A, whose mere presence produces excessive anxiety in Mr. Timothy Kleever who resides in the group home, may be transferred to work in another group home,

- *alter* the individual's reactions to the contributing stimulus events by teaching alternative ways of coping with these events, e.g., teaching Mr. Kleever anxiety reduction strategies,

- *introduce* instigating stimulus conditions for behaviors that compete with the challenging behaviors, e.g., if Ms. Donna Wards is frequently in a "bad mood" when she arrives at her vocational training program and is "set" to engage in challenging behaviors in response to minor sources of aggravation, routinely provide initial social or work experiences that create a "good mood."

When we identify and modify specific environmental *instigating* conditions, we are using individual centered interventions. *Individual Centered Behavioral Interventions* focus on proactive treatment and management of these specific *instigating* conditions that result in challenging behaviors. We want to increase the number of *instigating* influences for positive behaviors and to decrease the presence of those associated with challenging behaviors.

A focus on *instigating* factors associated with challenging behaviors may be new to some readers. Until recently, most behavior programs have concentrated on what happens after the challenging behavior occurs, that is, on behavioral *consequences.* In a similar manner, most research has evaluated *consequence* based interventions (Gardner et al., 1986).

As noted in Chapter Two when we discussed the potential causes of challenging behaviors, it was suggested that what happens before the behavior, the *antecedent,* is of critical importance. In fact, consequences only have an effect on behavior *relative to the antecedent context* in which these occur. If a person does not value social attention provided by some persons, in illustration, this consequence would not serve as a reinforcing condition. On the contrary, this person may find the attention of a particular peer who persist in attempts at social interaction to be aversive and thus an antecedent for challenging behaviors. Thus, a desired program strategy would involve modifying those *antecedents* that instigate challenging behaviors.

This program focus is:

* *less* intrusive with regards to the individual, and
* *more* preventive in focus.

This program focus does not imply that we are not concerned with the immediate *consequences* of challenging behaviors. Chapter Eight addresses the role of behavioral consequences.

Identifying Instigating Factors For Problem Behavior

As discussed in previous chapters, challenging behavior problems are influenced by such general environmental conditions as lack of privacy or lack of positive human interactions. Improvement in the general quality of the environment will have a therapeutic effect.

Antecedent modifications involving more person specific conditions can take many forms. They may involve changes in the nature and quality of social interactions, task related variables, methods of instructions, opportunities for choices, environmental structure, and other triggering and contributing antecedent events (Bambara et al., 1994).

Several methods may be used to assess the *instigating* factors for a person's challenging behaviors. Traditionally, behavior has been analyzed using an ABC (Antecedent-Behavior-Consequence) format. This method is helpful in identifying patterns that are fairly evident and infrequent. However, often the patterns of events *instigating* the behavior are complex and difficult to detect from the narrative information provided by this format.

A different observational format, a scatter plot analysis is described by Touchette and associates (1985). Using their method, the frequency of a challenging behavior over the course of the week(s) is plotted in graphic form against the time of day. With these data, one can visually detect when the problem behavior is most likely *and* least likely to occur and then note the differences present at those times to speculate about possible *instigating* factors. Once these conditions are identified, these may be modified or eliminated. Other conditions associated with minimal or no challenging behaviors can be substituted. Let's examine a simple example:

In the sample scatterplot below, it can be seen that the individual only has difficulty at two times in the day (between 7:00 and 9:00 in the morning and between 4:30 and 6:00 in the evening). Morning was the most difficult time for the individual. Of equal importance, no incidents of the behavior were noted at other times in the day or evening. In addition, the behavior did not occur on the weekends. The observer can examine the instigating factors present during these problem times, and note if these were absent during other times of the day and week.

In this case, the activities in the home at the problem times were quite intense. People were getting ready for work in the morning and preparing dinner in the evening. There generally were a number of people in the area of the kitchen or bathroom during these times of busy activities. Using this information, staff altered the person's schedule of getting up in the morning to insure that he would be ready for work before the rush. After work, he was provided choices of leisure activities that could be done alone or with one other person, and thus avoid the crowded activities. These environmental and schedule changes resulted in a dramatic reduction in the challenging behavior.

Sample Scatterplot (Touchette et al., 1985)				Person:			Date:	
Activity	Time	Mon	Tues	Weds	Thurs	Fri	Sat	Sun
	7.00							
	7.30							
	8.00							
	8.30							
	9.00							
	9.30							
	10.00							
	10.30							
	11.00							
	11.30							
	12.00							
	12.30							
	1.00							
	1.30							
	2.00							
	2.30							
	3.00							
	3.30							
	4.00							
	4.30	X	X	X	X	X		
	5.00	X	X	X	X	X		
	5.30	X	X	X	X	X		
	6.00							
	6.30							
	7.00							
	7.30							
	8.00							
	8.30							
	9.00							
	9.30							
	10.00							
	10.30							
	11.00							

Legend: no incidents (leave blank) low incidence (/)   medium incidence (X)   high incidence (fill in square)

A recent experience with Mr. James Hendricks provides an additional illustration of this proactive management strategy:

> After determining the time and location associated with high frequency challenging behaviors, further observations revealed that these behaviors followed verbal and physical prompts by a particular staff for James to complete the morning meal. Other staff members could provide similar prompts with positive results. Closer observation revealed that the staff provoking the outbursts was gruff and impatient in manner, in sharp contrast to the approach used by other staff. Transfer of this staff to another living area resulted in an immediate reduction in problem behaviors.

Gardner and associates (1986) noted that over time occurrence of specific challenging behaviors often are variable. On some occasions specific triggering conditions would result in the behaviors but at other times these seemingly similar conditions would not. They offer an expanded model of analysis, discussed in earlier Chapters, that examines a more complex range of both triggering and contributing events. In illustration of this expanded analysis, an individual following excessive caffeine intake from coffee was more likely to respond aggressively to staff corrective feedback than when he was caffeine free. The psychological state of heighten arousal produced by the caffeine served as a contributing stimulus event that combined with staff corrections to increase the likelihood of occurrence of the challenging behaviors.

Antecedent *contributing* stimulus conditions may serve either to facilitate or to inhibit the effects of specific triggering events. In addition to increasing the likelihood of challenging behaviors when exposed to triggering events, other contributing conditions can serve to decreased the likelihood of these challenging behaviors when exposed to these same triggering events. A person who occasionally uses aggression as a means of coping with unwanted directives from staff is more likely to behave aggressively when in an angry irritable mood. When in a relaxed positive mood, the person is less likely to behave aggressively when given similar unwanted directives.

A third method of data collection that is consistent with the Multimodal Contextual Behavior Analytic Assessment protocol described earlier is the functional analysis described by O'Neill, Horner, Albin, Storey, and Sprague, (1990). This format provides a comprehensive assessment of both *instigating events* and consequences of the challenging behaviors. This assessment guide not only provides information derived from a scatter plot but also information that would typically be available from an ABC chart.

Changing Specific Instigating Factors For Challenging Behaviors

Three options are available for reducing the effects of instigating conditions on challenging behaviors:

* *Removing* the instigating condition (permanently or temporarily),
* *Reducing* the instigating condition (permanently or temporarily), and
* *Altering* the instigating condition.

Let's look more closely at how each of these options might work. The question of selecting a specfic option is discussed later in the chapter. At this point, we will describe and illustrate each option.

Removing the Instigating Condition

It may be that the *instigating* condition is something that can be removed from the person's life without negative effects on the person or others around him/her.

Mr. Anthony Fells illustrates this approach.

Mr. Fells has an extreme fear of dogs. He recently moved to a group home with three other men and a large dog. Although the dog lives in the fenced-in area of the yard, its presence creates daily outbursts when Anthony is encouraged to spend time in the yard. If his peers agree to move the dog to another home, and to replace it with a cat, the source of Anthony's fear, agitated outbursts, and self-imposed isolation would be removed. If this is the only condition that instigates the negative behaviors, removal of the dog would represent a proactive management approach to problem solution.

The case manager, in consultation with the three other men, decided that the *instigating* condition could be removed temporarily from the group home. During the absence of the *instigating* factor, proactive treatment would be provided to increase Anthony's tolerance and ability to cope with the presence of dogs. The team concluded that it is not possible or desirable to shelter

Anthony from dogs for the rest of his life as he is likely to encounter dogs in the community. Treatment would include a desensitization program plus related coping skills training. Anthony would be taught to appropriately deal with concerns by talking out problems with others or by leaving the area if something is annoying. The treatment outcomes: the individual learns to tolerate dogs, learns coping skills, and the dog returns home.

Reducing the Aversiveness of the Instigating Condition

The *instigating* condition may involve levels of intensity. An assessment may indicate that an antecedent stimulus event must achieve a certain level of intensity before becoming a triggering event for a person's challenging behaviors. Lowering the intensity of the *instigating* condition would result in a reduction in the challenging behavior.

Sound level provides an illustration. Many people find it difficult to tolerate loud sounds. Such loud sounds may trigger behavioral outbursts in a person. If the sound is below a certain decibel level, the person does not react negatively as this level sound is not annoying. Excessive task demands represent a second example of a stimulus condition that varies in its aversiveness based on the number of demands made of a person. An individual may be able to tolerate a certain number of task demands without reacting with challenging behaviors. The person may react negatively when the number of demands exceeds the person's tolerance level.

The following examples address the question of whether we would reduce the *instigating* factor for challenging behaviors on a *temporary* or on a more *permanent* basis.

Ms. Susan Johnston, a young woman residing in a small group home, provides the first example.

Ms. Johnston displayed moaning and self abusive behavior whenever exposed to loud noises. Assessment revealed the approximate decibel level that resulted in these problem behaviors. With this information, staff was able to proactively manage her moaning and self-injury through controlling noise levels in home and school environments. She was not exposed to environments in which sound level could not be managed— the canteen at her work setting, her parents' home, the community at large. Even though successful in managing her challenging behaviors, her lifestyle was seriously restricted. Moreover, it was not determined why loud noises were so aversive to her and why she used self-injury as a means of removing or reducing these events. Further assessment obviously was needed to understand more fully and program for her challenging behaviors. Medical assessment revealed that Susan was having frequent migraine headaches. The pain and psychological distress associated with these served as a contributing instigating condition. When her headaches were severe, the addition of excessive noise served to produce the moaning and self-injury. These behaviors in turn resulted in staff reducing the loud noise. Medical treatment for the migraines was provided which in turn raised the threshold of sound levels that could be tolerated without her resorting to self-injury.

Even following treatment of the migraines, Ms. Johnston continued to be more sensitive to noise than most people. Therefore, she was taught various coping skills for use when confronted with loud noises. These included her leaving a noisy area when practical or requesting through sign language for sound levels to be lowered. Finally, she was moved to a less noisy work environment and also to a group home with quieter companions. Even after all these changes, she still had to deal with some loud sounds in some aspects of her life. Challenging behaviors, although reduced significantly, were not completely eliminated. She could tolerate noise levels in her home and school, and could also tolerate most community settings. There continued to be certain community environments such as movie theaters and sports events which she avoided because the sound levels were too high for her to tolerate without become upset. Overall, both the contributing (migraine headaches) and triggering (loud noise) instigating conditions were reduced and her tolerance for noise increased.

Mr. Jerry Stonewell provides a second example.

Mr. Stonewell engaged in temper outbursts when task demands were made. Since he was large, and his outbursts typically resulted in property destruction, his challenging behaviors were of considerable concern to staff. Assessment revealed that Jerry could deal with a certain number of task demands. When task demands exceeded this level of tolerance, he would become agitated. It became evident that staff were making excessive task demands of him. He had little control over his lifestyle, and most staff interaction focused on providing directives. He had little unscheduled free time, nor did he have positive, typical relationships with other adults. It appeared that staff spent excessive time supervising and instructing Jerry. His lifestyle did not represent a normalized environment for an adult.

The interventions consisted of changing Mr. Stonewell's lifestyle. Environmental features that served as instigating conditions for his challenging behaviors were modified. Jerry was provided more control and choices, thus minimizing the need for excessive directives. Additionally, time spent "in programs" was reduced. This provided normalized amounts of time to relax, relate to others as companions, and take part in activities of his choice. In addition to these proactive behavior management procedures involving environmental and program changes, a treatment component was added. Jerry was taught appropriate ways of expressing his anger and frustrations. By normalizing the number of type of directives provided, offering more choice and control, and teaching alternatives means of expressing his negative feelings, the challenging behaviors became infrequent occurrences.

The changes in Mr. Stonewell's life provides excellent demonstration of the *Individual Centered Behavioral Interventions* approach. We recognized that the *instigating* factor for his challenging behaviors related to a quality of life issue and that Jerry was justifiably displeased with his circumstances. We also demonstrated the value of teaching more effective anger management skills in providing him more control over his actions. Therefore, our interventions were selected to provide a normalized lifestyle. This in turn resulted in reduction of the conditions that instigated his challenging behaviors.

Altering the Instigating Conditions

Sometimes it is possible to alter the form of *instigating* conditions without any detriment to the individual or others around him. Through changing the form, we may effectively reduce or eliminate related challenging behaviors.

Ms. Ruth Poindexter provides an example of this approach.

Ms. Poindexter, a 37-year-old woman, would become extremely upset when asked to complete her chores in the group home. Her challenging behaviors included yelling and biting her hand, sometimes until it bled. Observation revealed that only certain types of demands *instigated* these behaviors. Staff who had worked with Ruth for an extended period provided excellent insight about the best way to approach her. This consisted of an initial explanation of why a task needed to be done and use of a joking manner when doing so. This interaction style most typically resulted in Ruth's cooperation. However, if instructed to do something with no explanation or good natured conversation, she typically became angry, began yelling, and if staff persisted, began to bite her hand. In our opinion, Ruth wanted to be treated as a peer rather than a client. Staff was encouraged to use a relaxed personable manner at all times when prompting her to complete various tasks. In addition, a self-monitoring checklist was developed with her assistance which pictorially depicted each of her routine daily household responsibilities. This provided Ruth with a concrete reminder of her daily activities. By sharing the completed checklist with staff at the end of the day, she was insured of personal time to chat as peers. When Ruth became lax in completing her responsibilities, staff would merely suggest in a nonprovocative manner that Ruth check her list. Finally, an alternative communication program was initiated to teach her to use pictures to express her emotions and concerns. This combination of interventions proved to be quite effective. This combination of supports provides another example in which normalization played an important role. The challenging behaviors were *instigated* by staff actions of dealing with her as a child rather than an adult. Although her behaviors were inappropriate, her reactions were easy to understand when viewed from her perspective.

Which Option Do We Choose?

We have discussed three approaches to changing *antecedent instigating* factors. How do we decide which option to choose? The following guidelines may be useful in making this decision.

Guideline 1: Best Interests of the Individual

We should consider initially what is in the best interests of the individual. For example, we may have someone who engages in challenging behaviors when prompted to bathe or shower. It is not in the person's best interest for us to say to that person that he/she need never clean with water again. That would be unhealthy and would certainly curtail a normalized social life. In this instance, removing the reminder with the result that the person may go days or weeks without appropriate personal hygiene would not be in the person's best interest.

In our earlier account of Ms. Susan Johnston whose challenging behaviors were triggered by loud noises, we decided that it would serve her best interest to restrict her lifestyle on a temporary basis by limiting her daily activities to environments in which the noise level could be controlled. It would not, however, have been ethically valid to have done this for the rest of her life. What made this approach acceptable was the fact that during the period of restriction, we were also providing relevant treatment to insure her eventual return to a more typical range of environments.

The *best interests of the individual* represents the priority guideline.

Guideline 2: Practicality

Sometimes it is just not practical to choose certain options. In our previous example involving Mr. Fell's fear of dogs, we knew it was not realistic to shield Anthony from dogs for the rest of his life. Nor could we alter the *instigating* condition (sight of a dog) that provoked the excessive fear and resulting self-imposed isolation. Therefore, practical concerns resulted in selection of treatment procedures to reduce Mr. Fell's fear of dogs.

Sometimes an option will be so practical that it shouts out to us. Our experience with Ms. Poindexter of changing the format of task demands from instruction to polite requests demonstrates this. It was relatively easy (and inexpensive) for staff to change their style of relating to Ms. Poindexter regarding tasks.

Practicality, however, should not be used as an excuse. This is particularly true when ethical issues are involved. We sometimes hear that it is not practical to change an *instigating* condition involved in producing challenging behaviors because of policies. In our opinion, a person's right to individual centered treatment should not be denied under the cloak of policy restrictions. The best interests of the individual compel us to provide the most normalized option.

Aren't We Letting The Individual "Get Away With It"

A frequent concern with an approach that uses proactive behavior management procedures as initial steps to influencing challenging behaviors is that the person is getting away with his/her inappropriate behaviors. Rightly so, it is pointed out, that some of the antecedents for challenging behaviors represent conditions or requirements that we all have to live with—task demands, time without staff attention, doing chores, following schedules and required routines. The opinion is stated that, rather than modifying the *instigating* factors, should we not require that the individual accept them.

These concerns are legitimate and can be addressed from two perspectives.

First, the *instigating* conditions for a person's challenging behaviors may be ones which should be changed as they are inappropriate or not normalized. Mr. Jerry Stonewell, discussed earlier, provides illustration of this perspective. Recall that his challenging behaviors were produced by excessive task demands. We would all agree that he was not getting away with anything when the number of directives were reduced and replaced by providing him increased control over his own environment. On the contrary, our approach merely insured that his lifestyle became more normative for his age.

Second, on a temporary basis, we may remove or reduce the *instigating* factors to allow the person time to develop tolerance for these conditions and other skills of coping with these factors.

This approach may be used, for example, in a work setting with a trainee who displays negative behaviors when reminded to remain at the work station and complete his work rather than roam around the facility. We may begin our intervention by requiring a small amount of work to be completed, gradually increasing the amount of work and time required to meet the work quota. At the same time, we maximize treatment effectiveness through good planning. This may include strategies such as offering a variety of work, mixing preferred activities with less preferred ones, and providing frequent short breaks throughout the work day. We may also teach the trainee to communicate in an appropriate manner his need for a break from the work routine. Finally, the types and amounts of reinforcers provided for work production as well as the schedule of providing these may be modified to better match his needs.

With this approach, we recognize the nature of the *instigating* factor and systematically alter these to approximate the standards required in the work setting.

Additional Strategies

Some additional strategies for modifying instigating conditions for challenging behaviors include:

*   *increasing* the frequency of antecedents for positive behaviors,
*   *teaching* new skills of coping with the instigating conditions, and
*   *shifting* consequences to encourage alternative prosocial behaviors.

Each is described.

Increasing Instigating Conditions for Positive Behaviors

Our examples have focused on assessment of those antecedents involved in *instigating* challenging behaviors and selecting procedures based on assessment results of changing those antecedents. Another important component of *Individual Centered Behavioral Interventions* consists of presenting antecedents that *instigate* positive behaviors.

We may work with someone who is quite demanding of staff attention and will act inappropriately when not interacting directly with staff. However, that person may also sit happily without any company if listening to favorite music. The availability of music *instigates* positive behavior. In this instance, a good strategy would involve providing access to favorite music during times when staff are busiest. This accomplishes the goal of increasing positive behavior which actually competes with the challenging behavior. In addition, we would plan to expand the range of *instigating* conditions for other positive behaviors that would reduce the person's excessive need for staff attention. After all, the individual's quality of life is limited if he/she is only behaving positively when listening to music or receiving staff attention. We may, as examples, (a) assist the person in developing other hobbies which would *instigate* positive behavior or (b) teach the person to work with staff in completing various activities.

Teaching New Skills

While working with *instigating* conditions, we also want to provide opportunities for the individual to learn new skills of dealing with these events. This approach is reviewed in detail in Chapter Eight. At this point, it is sufficient to state that an individual centered intervention plan would combine environmental changes with educational opportunities. It is the latter component which supports the person in gaining more control over his/her life.

It has been shown that challenging behaviors can be modified by changing other related behaviors (Helmstetter & Durand, 1990). This can be achieved by teaching alternative skills which serve the same function, or are functionally related or which provide the individual with increased skills in tolerance or coping.

When an individual is reacting negatively to certain events in the environment, the analysis of these events can be used to determine what skills an individual needs to learn that could either allow the individual to appropriately obtain the desired outcome (e.g., through communication or social skills training) or to learn to cope with the same events or be more tolerant to the events (e.g., through relaxation training or anger management training).

In sum, teaching alternative means that permit the individual to self-manage those conditions that result in challenging behavior is a key strategy in effective behavioral intervention. As noted, this topic is discussed further in Chapter Eight.

Shifting Consequences to Encourage Alternative Skill Use

The following represent approaches to shifting consequences to encourage alternative skill use.

Systematically Reinforce the Alternative Skill

For the alternative skill training to be effective, it is important to provide reinforcement for use of the new alternative skill. A variety of differential reinforcement procedures have been effectively used to increase the use of alternative or incompatible behaviors while simultaneously reducing the problem behavior.

To illustrate, if the individual is being taught to handle anger-provoking situations through use of communication rather than aggression, a critical factor in its success is the systematic reinforcement of the communication behavior.

Ensure Reinforcement Effectiveness

The new behavior must produce reinforcing consequences that are of equal or greater value to that previously resulting from the challenging behavior. Otherwise, there is no payoff for learning the new skill.

Make the Challenging Behavior Nonfunctional

Finally, the challenging behavior should no longer result in reinforcement. If the challenging behavior previously had resulted in valued social attention, this consequence must no longer follow challenging behaviors. Unless the individual has another way of getting the desired outcome and is able to use the new skill with equal effectiveness, the challenging behavior will continue as the predominate means of gaining attention. Under this scenario, the challenging behavior typically becomes more exaggerated in an attempt to obtain the desired consequence. This can be avoided if the new skill is well established and is being followed consistently with the reinforcing consequence desired by the person. Consistency in reinforcement of the desired behavior is the key.

Conclusion

When working with *instigating* factors, we use a positive approach to intervention. The key to effectiveness is to use assessment information as a basis for identifying relevant antecedent conditions and for selecting alternatives skills as effective means of gaining desired consequences. Program success entails not only elimination of the challenging behavior but also involves altering the environment to prompt positive behavior. In this manner we increase the individual's control over his or her life.

CHAPTER EIGHT

TEACHING PROSOCIAL SKILLS AS FUNCTIONAL REPLACEMENTS

Dorothy M. Griffiths and Jo Anne Nugent

Chapter Seven provided discussion of antecedent conditions that serve to instigate challenging behaviors. This Chapter describes the roles served by the *consequences* of these behaviors. Attention is given to those consequences that serve a reinforcing role, that is, those that add to the strength of challenging behaviors and define the purposes or functions served by these. Knowledge of these offers direction to interventions designed to reduce the behaviors.

Additionally, major attention is given to the manner in which positive consequences can be used to teach new competency skills that effectively replace challenging behaviors. This program focus addresses various personal skill deficits (e.g., coping, anger management, conflict resolution, social, leisure, work, communication) that represent *vulnerabilities* for the person.

Finally, brief attention is given to discussion of negative consequences that may be used to reduce challenging behaviors. As inappropriate use of negative consequences is inconsistent with the *Individual Centered Behavioral Interventions* approach, discussion of this topic will focus on the limitations of inappropriate use.

Until recently, behavioral approaches focused mainly on identifying and modifying consequences related to challenging behaviors. However, as Bambara et al. (1994) and Gardner et al. (1986) have stated, this focus may not produce desired results. The improvement in behaviors are dependent on the presence of a care giver to manage the consequences. In some instances, interventions involving negative consequence have been used to gain control over seriously dangerous behavior. The *Individual Centered Behavioral Interventions* approach, in contrast, seeks to teach new personal competencies and uses modification of antecedent instigating conditions as an initial strategy to reduce the challenging behaviors. This combination of positive approaches offers promise of being more effective in producing durable changes in the behaviors that the person uses to cope with various sources of provocation.

In Chapter Two, the three contexts in which challenging behaviors occur—context of *instigating* influences, context of personal and environmental *vulnerabilities*, and the context of consequences that define the *purpose or function* of behavior—were described. In assessing this third context, that of functionality, the following types of questions are raised: What does the person get out of the challenging behavior? What is the person trying to achieve with the behavior? What is the function of the behavior? In other words, what happens after the challenging behavior that is meaningful enough to the person (i.e., that he/she finds of sufficient value) to repeat the behavior when again confronted with related instigating conditions?

When we ask these questions, we attempt to understand the

person's *motivations*—what does the person find *reinforcing or enjoyable* and what does the person find *aversive or unpleasant*? If we can understand these, we can use this information to teach new ways of behaving that are more socially acceptable but still accomplish the same or similar purposes or goals for the person.

Personal Autonomy

The term personal autonomy means having independence and control over what happens to you as an individual. A crucial component of *Individual Centered Behavioral Interventions* is a commitment to providing behavioral supports that increase the person's self-control and choice in his/her life. *Therefore, interventions are designed to teach self-control, and not to increase external control over the individual.*

Interventions for challenging behaviors designed to change the *function* of the behavior are based on the assumption that behavior does serve a purpose for the individual, thus the term "functional" or "functionality." This assumption results in a philosophic view of respecting the person's motivational features. In illustration, if a person is aggressive, our primary focus is not on the aggression. Rather, our efforts are devoted to searching for the purpose served by the aggressive behavior. Is he being aggressive because he is being pressured to attend a program that he dislikes? Is he being aggressive in order to stop the taunts of a peer? Is he being aggressive because he is jealous of the attention given to a roommate? Only after understanding the function of the behavior are we able to select individual centered interventions designed to provide the person with alternative solutions to meeting the needs being expressed by the challenging behaviors.

All Behavior Has Meaning

All behaviors are performed for some reason. Even challenging behaviors of persons with significant mental health concerns serve a purpose. Successful resolution of challenging behaviors is based on determining the meaning or function of the behavior. With this information, we can assist the individual in selecting positive behaviors that can replace the challenging behavior or, at least, make it less likely that the challenging behavior will occur.

What happens if we merely try to eliminate the challenging behavior without developing alternative behaviors that will serve the same or similar *function* for the person?

First, it will be quite difficult to do this. The individual will likely cling to the challenging behavior because it serves a purpose for him/her. If so inclined, we may use restrictive and negative behavioral techniques to suppress the challenging behavior. This approach requires a high degree of control by staff over the individual and frequently is undertaken without understanding the person's purpose or motivation in engaging in these actions. Because the person's needs being expressed through the behavior remain unmet, two results are likely. First, as soon as we relax our behavioral controls over the individual, the challenging behavior is likely to recur. To successfully suppress the behavior, we must be consistent in using the negative consequences. This compromises the individual's quality of life. Also, it is not particularly practical.

Second, quite often an equally inappropriate replacement behavior begins to serve the same *function* as the challenging behavior we have suppressed. Because we have not taught the individual any new positive strategies, it is likely that other behaviors equally as problematic as the original behavior will occur.

It thus is crucial to the success of behavioral supports that we attend closely to the function or purpose of the behavior and use this information to provide effective interventions. As examples, if the behavior occurs as a means to escape or avoid an aversive situation, alternative means of accomplishing this purpose should be taught. If the behavior represents attempts to gain attention from a valued staff, alternatives means of soliciting social attention should be encouraged.

It should be recognized, as noted in Chapter Two, that a challenging behavior can be reinforced by its consequences without the person's awareness that reinforcement is occurring. That is, challenging behavior may not be premeditated or represent a planned act. Reinforcement can occur automatically, and be independent of the person's intent or awareness. In fact, most challenging behaviors presented by persons with mental retardation and mental health concerns do not represent intentional or premeditated acts but rather occur automatically when specific instigating conditions are present. The person may be unable to describe the intent or purpose of the challenging actions. Rather, the behavior occurs as it has worked a sufficient number of times in the past (that is, has resulted in reduction of anxiety, removed an unwanted directive, resulted in valued social attention, etc.) and thus has become an automatic or habitual way of responding when these instigating conditions occur. As a result, no therapeutic objective is served by "blaming" the person for his/her behaviors or responding to it in a punitive manner.

Our individual centered approach initially seeks to understand the function(s) served by the behavior along with the instigating and vulnerability contexts in which these occur. Supports are then provided for the person (a) to develop an awareness of his/her motivations and (b) to acquire alternative means of relating to these.

Of course, some challenging behaviors for some persons may indeed represent planned, deliberate, or intentional acts. Our approach uses this information in supporting the individual in learning both alternative prosocial skills along with the personal motivation to use these newly acquired actions.

Individual Preferences and Ambitions

To truly support the individual, we should accept the validity of the individual's preferences and ambitions for his/her own way of life. We should honor the importance of those goals for the person, and support the individual in understanding and fulfilling these. This may not be how *we* want to live our lives but if the individual expresses preferences, his/her choice should be respected whenever possible. We should attempt to understand the person's preferences and ambitions in the context of the individual's right to self determination. Of course, we cannot support goals that are illegal or directly harmful to the person or others.

Respecting the person's preferences does not mean, however, that we accept the behavior which is being used to achieve these. Our supports consist of teaching new socially acceptable ways for the individual to achieve the same or similar goals. A variety of educative approaches are discussed in later section of this chapter for use in maximizing learning of new behaviors while still respecting the individual's autonomy.

Reinforcement and Punishment

As noted earlier, a discussion of *consequences* involves consideration of *reinforcement* and *punishment*. Consequences of behavior that make challenging behaviors more like to occur under similar conditions of instigation (i.e., increases its strength) may involve either (a) *positive reinforcement* or (b) *negative reinforcement*. Positive reinforcement occurs when challenging behaviors result in something that is pleasant, pleasing, rewarding, or valuable to the person (e.g., social attention, social approval, food, access to favorite activity, money). Negative reinforcement occurs when challenging behaviors result in the reduction, termination, or avoidance of something aversive, unpleasant, or uncomfortable to the person (e.g., reduction in fear or anxiety, reduction in pain, removal of unwanted directive, avoidance of unpleasant scheduled activity). An understanding of the process of negative reinforcement is critical *as a significant majority of challenging behaviors* serve the purpose of reducing, terminating, or avoiding conditions that the person finds unpleasant or aversive. As noted earlier, a major focus of diagnostic and intervention efforts is on identifying and changing these conditions as a means of removing the motivation for the challenging behaviors. If this is not possible, the focus becomes that of reducing the aversive conditions to the extent possible in addition to teaching alternatives ways of responding to the conditions that remain.

Punishment refers to occurrence of consequences following challenging behaviors that make the behavior *less likely* to occur again under similar instigating conditions. Examples of these punishing consequences are verbal reprimands, withdrawal of privileges, ignoring a person who enjoys attention, and isolating the person from a reinforcing environment. As noted earlier, the major focus of the *Individual Centered Behavioral Interventions* approach is on use of positive reinforcement procedures to teach and strengthen competency skills to replace challenging behaviors.

Choosing Replacement Behaviors

Which behaviors should be selected to teach as replacements for the challenging behaviors? We want replacement behaviors that will endure over time and, in most instances, to serve the *function(s)* served by the challenging behaviors. We want behaviors that are socially appropriate and thus have a high probability of being reinforced and repeated by the individual. Following are some guidelines for this selection process.

Choose Replacement Behaviors That Are Normative

First, we choose replacements for the challenging behaviors that are typical for any person of the individual's age and culture. In doing this, we are ensuring that the replacement behaviors will be acceptable to and thus reinforced by others in the person's environments. Also we increase the probability that the replacement behaviors will be appropriate in a range of environments, thus facilitating generalization.

Choose Replacement Behaviors That Will Be Sustained Outside Training Settings

We want to choose behaviors that are valued by persons other than those involved in training. The purpose is to teach behaviors that will be maintained when training is completed. These behaviors will be naturally reinforced in the person's daily life. This training objective is based on what has been called the "Relevance of

Behavior Rule" (Allyon & Azrin, 1968).

For example, we can teach an adult to sit on both hands to replace the challenging behavior of hand biting. This may work in a clinical setting to effectively compete with the hand biting since staff is available to prompt this behavior and to provide immediate reinforcement for it. However, the individual is not likely to receive much positive reinforcement for this behavior from most people outside the clinical setting.

If we teach a useful coping skill such as taking a deep breath and holding his hands together when upset as a replacement for the hand biting, this alternative can be used in a variety of different settings and is likely to receive positive feedback by most people.

Choose Replacement Behaviors That Are Portable Across Environments

If we choose a behavior that can be used in different environments, the individual will have more opportunities to use the skill and be reinforced following its use. This will add to the strength and durability of the replacement skills.

Choose Replacement Behaviors That Are Easy To Learn

We are working with people who have diminished abilities to learn. A replacement behavior that is complicated and is learned slowly over a lengthy period of time is not very appealing to the individual The individual will likely become discouraged before the skill is learned and will abandon it.

Choose Replacement Behaviors That Are Easy To Perform

Likewise, we want to choose a behavior that the individual can easily perform. The individual will more likely choose to use that behavior. For example, we may be working with someone who screams to avoid an activity. If we teach the individual who has severe speech difficulties a simple hand signal for "Please let me have a break," the individual will find that easy to use. If the individual must say a long sentence such as "Please may I have a break now," this may prove to be quite difficult. Chances are that the individual will prefer to use the scream which is quick and takes relatively little effort (Horner & Day, 1991).

Choose Replacement Behaviors That Are Equivalent

Equivalent can be defined as equal in meaning. In most instances, we want to choose a replacement behavior that will have the same meaning for the individual as the negative behavior. In other words, it serves the same *function*. If an individual uses a challenging behavior to gain special staff assistance with a difficult task, a replacement behavior that accomplishes the same results should be taught.

Choose Replacement Behaviors That Can Be Self-Managed

When possible, teach replacement behaviors that the individual can initiate without requiring prompting or reinforcement from others. These are called self-managed activities. Self-managed behaviors are important because the individual can function without being excessively dependent on others to provide supports.

If a challenging behavior is functional in obtaining immediate staff assistance and attention, it would be best to teach a replacement skill that the person could initiate and enjoy without requiring staff presence and feedback. This is more realistic since staff cannot always provide immediate assistance or attention. It also enhances the individual's independence. Teaching the individual to operate a tape recorder represents an example of a self-managed replacement skill. The individual could listen to favorite music at times when staff are busy. The individual might even do this in the same location as the staff, thus encouraging a sense of companionship. Of course, this guideline is only applicable if the replacement behavior still serves the same or similar *function* as the challenging behavior, that is, will meet the person's motivational needs.

Choose Replacement Behaviors That Are Incompatible

It is physically impossible or difficult to perform some activities at the same time. For example, you cannot play the piano and draw a picture with your hands simultaneously. When appropriate, a replacement behavior is selected that is physically incompatible.

We may be working with an adult who bites his hands until they break the skin. If we teach the person to perform an activity which requires use of both hands such as typing on a computer, hand biting becomes impossible during typing times. Again, this will only be effective if the replacement skill has the same or equally valued *function* as the negative behavior. If the hand biting is being done to modulate pain, then typing on a computer is not an equivalent activity. However, if hand biting is done to express boredom, then our replacement skill can eliminate boredom and also the physical possibility of hand biting.

Summary

Obviously, there are many facets of replacement behavior to consider. By following the suggested or similar guidelines, we increase our chances of successfully replacing the challenging behavior. In addition, the individual gains more control over his/her life.

Effective Strategies For Teaching Alternative Behaviors

Once we have chosen the replacements skills, the next task is to teach these in an effective and efficient manner. Following are some suggestions to accomplish this objective.

Build Rapport With The Individual

Before a staff member attempts to implement a training program, it is valuable that rapport be developed with the person being taught. Rapport means a relationship in which there is mutual trust. The individual must know the trainer, like the trainer, and trust the trainer. Likewise, the trainer must know the individual, like the individual, and care about the individual's goals. This will maximize the effectiveness of the teaching.

It makes sense that an individual will learn better from a person he/she knows and trusts. This is the same for all of us. At the beginning of training, time should be spent to develop this rapport.

Choose a Trainer Who Is Valued

A trainer who has a positive relationship with an individual serves as a positive reinforcer (Carr, McConnachie, Levin, & Kemp, 1989). The approval of the trainer will be meaningful and important to the individual. This will increase the impact of any training efforts.

A particular staff member may have a negative history with the person being trained. The staff may have used punishment procedures with the individual. The staff may have a negative, nonreinforcing personality or the staff may not even like the individual being trained. Such staff will have a lower probability of being perceived by the individual as a positive reinforcer. Training is enhanced if the training staff is positive, likes the person being training, and has a positive (or neutral) history with the individual.

Enrich The Environment

It is valuable that training occur in an enriched environment. How we enrich the environment will depend on the function of the challenging behaviors being replaced. If the person is acting negatively to receive special privileges, we want to provide these special privileges when the replacement skill is displayed. If the person's challenging behaviors are produced by a generally boring existence, we want to maximize the stimulating opportunities in the environment and teach appropriate ways of accessing these.

Build On Existing Skills

As part of our assessment, we determine the individual's current repertoire of skills. Training will be more effective if we can expand on these skills to develop more acceptable behaviors for the individual to achieve his/her goals.

Attempts at teaching a totally new skill which has no foundation in the individual's current repertoire will be more difficult. It is slower, more frustrating for the individual, and less likely to result in success.

Consider Time, Location, and Conditions of Training

For teaching to be successful, the individual should be in the best possible physical health and frame of mind. If we know the person well, we should be able to choose the time, place, and conditions that will be the most positive for the individual.

We provide training at that time of day at which the individual is rested and alert. We all have our own natural daily rhythms, including peak times for performance. Try to choose a peak time for the individual. As well, it may be helpful to enhance an individual's good mood before teaching. Therefore, we may begin with an introductory activity that is a particular favorite or is relaxing, such as having a cup of tea and a quiet conversation. The positive mood created will serve as an instigating condition for appropriate involvement in the training activities.

Sometimes we cannot choose the ideal timing for the program because it must be carried out whenever the problem behavior occurs. However, we can attempt to control other factors. If possible, we can choose a setting with less distractions and a comfortable climate.

Whatever we can do that will increase the individual's cooperation and enjoyment will benefit the training experience.

Control Antecedent Instigating Stimuli

As emphasized, *Individual Centered Behavioral Interventions* recognize the importance of both *antecedents and consequences.* To increase the effectiveness of consequences, we also insure that antecedents are controlled. Remember that specific antecedents can have considerable influence over specific behaviors. We may design a great teaching program and follow all the recommended guidelines only to discover that the program is not effective. It may be that the presence of instigating conditions are triggering behaviors that compete with occurrence of the trained replacement behaviors.

For example, we may be teaching a individual to use language to express anger and frustrations. However, peers may interrupt the training by teasing the individual. This teasing may trigger swearing and aggressive action. Therefore, in spite of our efforts to teach appropriate anger management skills, the *instigating* conditions for the challenging behaviors continue to trigger these actions. In this instance, initial training of anger management and related coping skills should be conducted in a setting free of taunts of peers. Following success in a training setting, the taunts will be introduced gradually, while prompting and reinforcing the newly learned competing behaviors. These coping replacements may, as examples, consist of taking a deep breathe, ignoring the taunts, walking away from the peers, or seeking staff assistance. Through gradually introducing the instigating conditions (taunts) for the challenging behaviors and supporting the person in engaging in the replacement actions in the presence of these, the person discovers that the replacement behaviors work in obtaining the desired consequences.

Strategies For Specific Functions

We have suggested that the major functions served by challenging behaviors are those of obtaining *positive consequences* and avoiding, reducing, delaying, or escaping from *negative consequences*. We now look at each of these functions and offer strategies related to each.

Positive Reinforcement

One purpose of challenging behavior is to produce positive reinforcement for the individual. In other words, the *consequence* of the behavior is something that the individual likes, enjoys, and wishes to experience again.

Throughout the previous section on choosing replacement skills, we emphasized the importance of choosing skills that would result in equal, if not greater, reinforcing consequences than would the challenging behavior.

To accomplish this, we complete a thorough assessment as described in Chapters Three and Four. We want to know what is happening after the behavior that might be positively reinforcing for the individual. At this point, it is important to remember that positive reinforcement is individually defined. Frequently we see individuals acting inappropriately to gain staff attention. The attention may be quite negative to our eyes, e.g., scolding, reprimands, and physical intervention such as restraints. However, for the individual, this staff involvement may in fact serve as a positive reinforcer. In other words, what may be most important to the individual is human interaction, even if that interaction appears negative.

In actual fact, individuals who seek attention, even if they do so inappropriately, offer frequent opportunity for us to teach replacement skills. If a person is desirous of human contact, we can certainly use our presence as a major positive reinforcer for teaching. At the same time, we seek ways to enrich the environment in general so that the individual has different reinforcement options.

Sensitivity theory is a relatively new concept which helps us to further understand positive reinforcement (Reiss & Havercamp, 1997). This theory states that there are wide individual differences in response to specific events that may have reinforcement qualities.

Individuals differ in the type of events that are reinforcing as well in the amount of any reinforcing conditions that is sufficient to impact on the preceding behavior. For example, one person may only need a smile from a staff person to continue with an appropriate activity. Another person may need the staff to come over, enthusiastically comment on the performance of the activity, and offer a pat on the shoulder. This example is useful in understanding why some people appear to be "needy" in that they require constant attention and reassurance from others while others are more independent and require only a minimal amount of recognition.

As well, some people may be more susceptible to stress and anxiety and will act inappropriately to remove or reduce even small amounts of stress. Others may be able to tolerate all but the most life threatening situations without engaging in challenging behaviors as attempts to terminate or reduce the aversive conditions.

Reiss and Havercamp (1997) also suggested that we cannot assume that everyone is equally motivated by being happy or other seemingly universal sources of reinforcement. While some persons may strive for happiness, others may be unmotivated to attain it.

This theory reminds us that we should know a person well to be able to design programs dealing with the *function* of behavior. We should know what is positively reinforcing to the person and how much of a specific reinforcer is required to be meaningful.

As suggested earlier, some challenging behaviors serve the purpose of gaining access to various forms of *stimulation*. These typically occur when the person is in a relatively boring and unstimulating environment. To change these behaviors, we can increase the source of stimulation in the environment. This may include increasing the availability of activities or environmental components that provide access to these. It may involve increasing sensory stimulation by providing music or television or by providing more variety of environmental stimulation. Finally, we can increase the number, variety, and quality of human interactions.

Accompanying these environmental changes should be an effort to increase the individual's personal abilities to access appropriate stimulation. We can teach a new hobby, how to use a radio, or how to use the telephone to call family or friends as means of increasing independence. By increasing the potential sources of positive stimulation and the skills to access these sources, challenging behaviors engaged in as a means of gaining stimulation should be reduced or eliminated.

Negative Reinforcement

As noted, a second class of consequences that reinforce challenging behaviors are those involved in avoidance, reduction, delay, or escape from the unpleasantness associated with persons, activities, or places or with a range of internal states such as pain, disquieting thoughts and perceptions, and uncomfortable emotions such as anxiety or dysphoria. In our clinical experiences, most challenging behaviors gain strength as a result of negative reinforcement. Thus, assessment of those aversive conditions that motivate a person's challenging behaviors is needed to understand and program for these behaviors.

We begin by looking at what the person is trying to escape from, reduce, or avoid. Is it something that he/she has every right to find aversive and therefore to terminate? If so, we should remove the aversive condition.

> For example, staff may be taking all the residents of the group home to a basketball game. One individual in the home may dislike basketball and crowds. In an attempt to avoid these aversive conditions, challenging behaviors may be used by the person. In our view, the person should have the right to refuse. Staff should revise the planned outing so that the person may select an alternative one of his choice. Of course, even in this instance, the person should be taught and encouraged to expressed his dislikes in a more acceptable fashion.

On other occasions, a person may engage in challenging behaviors to avoid activities or events that are natural aspects of a life of increased independence. In these instances, after identifying the aversive conditions that motivate the challenging behaviors, a training program to teach increased tolerance of these conditions along with other coping strategies can be undertaken

Challenging Behaviors As Alternative Forms of Communication

As noted earlier, verbal communication is one of the most fundamental elements of being human. People who do not have effective verbal communication skills will use whatever other means are available to them to get their point across. Think of your own use of pantomime the last time you communicated with someone who did not speak any English!

It is well documented that the lower the level of communication skills that someone possesses, the higher the frequency of challenging behaviors (Carr et al., 1989). Challenging behavior can be the person's way of expressing: "I am in pain," "Pay attention to me," "I don't want to do this," "This is too difficult for me," "Give me more of that candy," or any other personal reasons. If assessment indicates that the person has difficulty communicating his/her concerns, needs, wishes, or desires and engages in challenging behaviors in response to these, alternative communicative behaviors should be taught as functional replacements.

Two points relate specifically to teaching communication skills. First, a thorough evaluation is required to determine what form of communication would be best taught to the individual. This can depend on the person's intellectual skills, physical skills, and the skills of the teachers. We may teach more than one form, such as vocal, signing and/or picture cards.

Second, we want to create as many communication opportunities as possible. In this way, the person can practice new skills and receive a higher frequency of positive reinforcement for appropriate communication. This means that we will want to have as many people as possible interacting with the individual. We want these people to be highly responsive to all communication attempts. We also want an enriched environment to provide many things to communicate about (Carr et al., 1989).

How Functions Interact

Challenging behaviors may at various times serve both to reduce aversive conditions and to produce positive consequences. For example, a man may become aggressive whenever he is requested to go to work. The aggression may fulfill two functions: *avoid-*

ance, since the aggression results in his staying home and avoiding a disliked work environment and *positive reinforcement* because during the day at home he watches television. To develop an effective treatment plan, we would need to address both functions. We could support him in finding a job he really enjoys (dealing with avoidance and positive reinforcement). Additionally, we could teach him a more appropriate alternative to aggression to express his needs

We should also be aware that the function of a behavior can change over time (Luiselli, 1996). A woman may initially begin head banging whenever she has a headache because the pain is reduced temporarily. Staff will undoubtedly respond immediately to the head banging. If we discover that she is having headaches, we can teach her to communicate this to us. We will then provide medication to relieve the headaches. However, she may continue head banging because it results in valued staff attention. The original *function* of pain reduction has been dealt with successfully. Nonetheless, we now have a new function which has developed and our interventions would be expanded to take this into account.

This suggest ongoing assessment is needed to insure that we understand the current *functions* of behaviors and how these may interact.

Conclusion

We have now looked at both the *antecedent instigating* factors and the *consequences* that influence behavior. In Chapter Nine, we describe a step by step approach to teaching replacement skills. As noted, an understanding of the "why" or "cause" of behavior is complex. Our interventions also may be complex, combining approaches that deal with instigating, vulnerability, and maintaining influences. In addressing the complexity of challenging behaviors, we are in a better position to ensure that our interventions enhance the personal autonomy of the individual.

CHAPTER NINE

TRAINING APPROACHES FOR TEACHING PROSOCIAL SKILLS

Dorothy M. Griffiths

In the previous chapter, the teaching of prosocial skills was offered as a means for decreasing vulnerabilities for problem behavior through providing alternative skills as functional replacements. This chapter continues that discussion by providing step by step strategies for teaching these prosocial replacement skills.

As discussed previously, challenging behaviors serve a purpose for the individual. Challenging behaviors produce a desired object, interaction, or activity or may represent an attempt to avoid or escape an undesired activity, interaction, environment, or other aversive conditions. Persons with developmental disabilities often lack appropriate skills to achieve these desired outcomes in an appropriate way. The challenging behavior may be the only means that the person has of influencing or changing social interactions or environments.

Treatment studies have shown that challenging behaviors may be reduced by rewarding alternative desired behaviors that serve the same purpose for the individual. It is important to note that we are not talking about just providing more reinforcement for *any* appropriate behavior. The alternative behavior taught and reinforced is one that serves the same purpose as the problem behavior. This requires initial identification of the motivation for the challenging behavior. The individual is then taught an alternative action that can become equally as effective in bringing about the desired outcome.

Deficits in appropriate communication skills represent a significant vulnerability for many persons with developmental disabilities. In the absence of appropriate means of communication to make needs or desires known, challenging behaviors may be used to produce results that could normally be achieved through language or augmentative communication methods.

In many situations, it is sufficient to teach a person an appropriate means of producing the outcome previously obtained through a challenging behavior. This requires that the new behavior be reinforced at the same rate, intensity and in as many situations as the challenging behavior had been. However, sometimes what the person wants cannot be provided in the manner desired by the person. In these situations, such skills as tolerance to delay, relaxation, or anger management may need to be taught.

Step One: Select A Relevant Replacement Behavior

There are several reasons to teach new skills as a major approach of a behavior intervention plan. These include:

- To provide appropriate ways of gaining or obtaining a desired object, activity, or interaction which the person currently is receiving through a challenging behavior.

- To provide an appropriate means to achieve sensory input or a pleasant internal state which the person currently is achieving through a challenging behavior.

- To provide appropriate ways of escaping or avoiding an inter-action, environment, or activity that the person currently is escaping or avoiding through challenging behaviors.

- To provide appropriate means for the individual to escape or avoid an unpleasant internal or sensory state that the person currently achieves through challenging behavior.

Let's take an example of each:

- *To provide appropriate ways of gaining or obtaining a desired object, activity, or interaction which the person currently is receiving through challenging behaviors.*

> Mr. Paul Smith hits his head on his wheelchair when he wants staff to attend to his needs. His staff thought at first that Mr. Smith wanted attention. However, staff discovered that just talking to him was not what Mr. Smith was seeking. He would continue the behavior until staff got him a drink, or changed the TV, or put on his music. A skills training program of teaching alternative means of communicating these various motivations is needed.

- *To provide appropriate ways to achieve sensory input or a pleasant internal state which the person currently is achieving through challenging behaviors.*

> Mr. John Alexander pokes his finger in his eye. He has done it so hard and so often that there is concern about permanent damage. It appears that he does this to provide some self-

stimulation. He can create a visual image (like stars) by pushing on his eye. The function of this behavior is therefore to increase sensory stimulation. The staff noted that he did not do this all the time but only when he was left too long without an activity. It was hypothesized that the behavior served to provide stimulation when bored. Mr. Alexander had no independent leisure skills. When staff were not available, he used the only behavior he had learned to entertain himself. Teaching alternative skills of gaining stimulation becomes the focus of Mr. Alexander's treatment program.

* *To provide appropriate ways of escaping or avoiding an interaction, environment, or activity that the person currently is escaping or avoiding through challenging behaviors.*

Mr. Chris Dowrick was referred for excessive masturbation. He would begin to masturbate throughout the day, often in public places throughout the house. His counselor would redirect him to his room whenever this behavior began. An ABC analysis was carried out for one week. The data revealed that he began to masturbate following demands to do the dishes, do his laundry, or set the table. The behavior did not occur unless there was a demand. Because he was sent to his room when he began to masturbate, the behavior was negatively reinforced when he avoided doing the undesired tasks. The staff of the group home worked with Mr. Dowrick to teach him how to choose tasks he preferred to do around the house and to tolerate doing some less preferred tasks on occasion.

- *To provide appropriate means for the individual to escape or avoid an unpleasant internal or sensory state that the person currently achieves through challenging behaviors.*

Miss Alicia Smith constantly has her hand in her mouth. She sucks on her hand so much that it has become infected and callused. Investigation showed that Miss Smith's medication caused increased thirst, and the staff concluded that the hand mouthing was perhaps her way of lubricating her mouth. Several strategies were considered: (a) change of medication, (b) more frequent refreshments, (c) teaching her a means of indicating her need for fluids, and (d) adapting the environment (handle on the refrigerator) so she can have access to fluids whenever she needs them.

Step Two: Identify The Specific Skill To Be Learned

Although a challenging behavior may be motivated to obtain or escape/avoid some event, the behavior does not occur all the time. As discussed in earlier chapters, the behavior may be more likely to occur in the presence of specific people, only in certain environments, when task x is presented but not when task y is presented, only at specified times of the day, or only when the person is sick. Thus the skills needed as replacement skills must be context specific.

Listed below are three common examples of specific replacement skills to replace challenging behaviors:

- *Teach skills to allow the individual to appropriately communicate a desired outcome.*

Mr. Bob Gallager can speak in sentences and appears to be able to make his needs known. However, when faced with anger provoking situations, such as being teased, Mr. Gallager tends to use his fists instead of his words to express anger. Staff taught him to appropriately express anger when faced with specific situations that were particularly provoking to him.

- *Teach skills of altering the environment to produce a desired outcome or avoid an unpleasant event.*

Mr. Irwin Williams is very sensitive to noise. He reacts to loud noises (e.g., a plane flying overhead or loud voices in a crowd) by becoming self-injurious. He hits at his ears until someone intervenes. He is removed to a different and quieter situation when the behavior occurs. Mr. Williams has learned that self-injury results in escape from the intolerable noises. As part of his behavior plan, the staff taught Mr. Williams to put on Walkman earphones whenever he was confronted with a noise. He then would listen to soothing music that would distract him from the outside noises.

- *Teach appropriate means of coping with such unpleasant situations as delays, tension, and anger that may be unavoidable.*

Mr. Marshall Ford engaged in violent outbursts every time he had to visit a doctor. Marshall showed considerable anxiety before the visits. He did not sleep, he would pace the floor and he would begin to rock. The staff decided to use a desensitization procedure. They talked to him about what frightened him. Because Mr. Ford had limited ability to describe his feelings, pictures were used to find out what frightened him. They next took him for brief nonthreatening visits. He was taught deep breathing exercises to use when he was getting upset. Before the visits began, staff explained exactly what would happen to him during the visit. For the first few times, staff only went into the waiting room and stayed for a short time. He was reinforced for using calm behavior. The next few times they actually saw the doctor for only a talk. Again he was reinforced for using his calm behavior. Gradually they began to introduce a few of the less frightening parts of the visits. This graduated exposure continued until he no longer showed anxiety or outburst during the doctor visits.

In addition to the relevance of the behavior to the function of the behavior, the behavior must also have relevance to the person's life. The following criteria for choosing relevant behaviors have been suggested by Sailor, Goetz, Anderson, Hunt, and Gee (1988). The skill should:

- be desired by the individual,
- be immediately useful,
- be able to be used frequently,
- be useful in increasing independence and integration opportunities,

- allow the individual to interact in a number of different situations,
- be taught by more than one person,
- be learned where the skill will be used, and
- be as age appropriate as possible.

Step Three: Identify Components of Skills Teaching

A teaching plan for any specific behavior would include the following components:

- *Description of the natural cues that trigger the desired behavior.*

Identify what typically would cue or prompt the behavior you are selecting to teach. For example, the natural cue for the time to wash you hands for dinner could be when the table is being set. A natural cue for not interrupting is when two people are talking. It is helpful to identify the natural cues so that the individual can be taught to use the natural prompts to initiate or inhibit behavior.

- *Description of the prompts used by the instructor to ensure that the desired behavior does occur in the presence of the triggering cue.*

When shaping a behavior, it important to encourage the behavior using prompts. Prompts can be verbal ("pick up the pillow"), gesture (pointing to the pillow) or physical (assisting the person to pick the pillow up). Initially it may be important to use all levels of prompts, first fading physical prompts, then verbal prompts and last . the gestural prompts. A prompt can be faded by giving less physical assistance or minimizing the verbal or gestural prompts until they can be eliminated entirely without a loss of performance.

Modeling the behavior is another excellent way to prompt the behavior to occur. Show the person how to do the behavior and then request imitation. The behavior is demonstrated for the individual and key aspects of the behavior are emphasized through comment.

*   *Description of the reinforcing consequences that follow the desired behavior.*

For a behavior to be learned, it must be reinforced. Reinforcement is very personal. What is reinforcing to one individual might not be reinforcing to another person. Therefore the selection of the reinforcer for a behavior is based on what a person likes and would work to achieve. Reinforcers can be social, tangible, activity, or tokens or combinations of these. Social reinforcement is generally paired with all other reinforcers.

During instruction, it is important to provide reinforcement for improvement in skill performance. Initially a continuous schedule of reinforcement is used in which attempts are reinforced each and every time the behavior occurs. However, behavior in the real world is reinforced only some of the time. This is called an intermittent schedule of reinforcement. Thus it is important to introduce a reinforcement schedule into the training that is as natural as possible. This is accomplished by thinning the reinforcement schedule, or moving it from a continuous to an intermittent schedule in a gradual manner.

There are two reasons why this change from continuous to intermittent reinforcement should be implemented. First, if the person has been reinforced for using alternative behaviors to aggression, and if the reinforcement is faded too quickly, extinction related aggression can occur. Second, if the reinforcement is faded too quickly so that too many repetitions of the behavior go unreinforced, the effect of the reinforcement can be lost. When that occurs, it is necessary to start the training again at an earlier stage and then build up again.

In some situations, fading the reinforcement is difficult because the individual has little if any tolerance for delayed reinforcement. This can be built into the program.

Let's see how this was done in the following example:

> Mr. William Bush had learned to request the end of a difficult or undesired interaction. However, he wanted it to end immediately. Unfortunately, with some interactions, immediate termination was impossible. For example, Mr. Bush would demand that he wanted out of a car immediately while driving in the center lane of the freeway. Staff taught Mr. Bush to tolerate delay through use of two methods. For some activities, they would respond to his requests to escape by immediate praise and recognition of his request followed by an instruction "Yes, we will stop this activity as soon as we finish this one (later two, three....)" until an appropriate delay was tolerated. For other activities, the delay was linked to time. Following his request, he was asked to wait for 30 seconds, 1 minute, 5 minutes etc. until an appropriate time was tolerated. At these times, he was reinforced immediately. Following training, Mr. Bush came to tolerate a reasonable delay in having his requests honored.

Other important teaching strategies include *role playing* and *performance feedback.*

Role Playing

One approach that is very effective in teaching prosocial skills is role playing. Role playing involves acting out situations during training so that the individual can witness and practice new roles to play when confronted with problematic situations. A variety of different situations can be presented and a range of behaviors can be taught.

Performance Feedback

In combination with the above strategies, the person providing the instruction can provide specific feedback following specific behavior. For example, "I like how you asked for help when you were having difficulty with your lunch." Be specific in giving feedback. It is generally a good idea to provide positive comments about the behavior and then, if necessary, suggest a way to improve the behavior. For example, "It was great that you came over to ask for help with your job. Next time if I am on the telephone, please wait until I finish before you ask. Then I can hear everything you are saying."

Performance feedback can also include providing the person information regarding the impact of his or her behavior on others. For example, "John, how do you think someone would feel when you yell at them like that?" or conversely, when showing a prosocial behavior, "How would your friends feel when you arrive on time for the movie?"

Step Four: Shape The Behavior

Most skills are complex. There are many subskills or steps involved in these complex skills. Complex skills may be taught by systematically reinforcing approximations of the behavior. The teaching approach may differ depending on the dimension that is being reinforced:

• Some skills are taught by progressively reinforcing actions that are more and more like the final desired behavior.

• Some skills are taught by altering behavioral dimensions such as intensity, rate, or duration (e.g., tolerating delays).

At the beginning of a skill training program, the person may only have the rudimentary approximations of a desired skill. The instructor can identify some components of the behavior that exists as a beginning step. Then the behavior is shaped gradually. In many situations, the skill can be broken down into smaller steps. Each step is taught and combined sequentially to make a whole. The teaching steps must be small enough to be attainable without frustration, but large enough to be encouraging. Some steps are more difficult to achieve and may take longer periods of time. If the person gets stuck on a step, it may be necessary to move back a step and then proceed.

Task Analysis

Some of the skills are best taught by breaking the skill into its component parts. For example, a young man's aggressive behavior may be triggered by the need for staff assistance to complete his morning chores. By teaching him independence in these skill areas, thc need for ongoing staff assistance would be eliminated and hence the triggering events for the aggression would be removed. To prepare for teaching, the staff may conduct a task analysis on each of the assigned chores. The task analysis for making a bed with a duvet cover is as follows:

Step 1. Take the pillows off the bed.
Step 2. Pull the blankets to thc bottom of the bed.
Step 3: Smooth out the bottom sheet.
Step 4: Pull the top sheet up and straighten it.
Step 5: Pull the duvet cover up and straighten it.
Step 6: Fold the top of the sheet over the duvet cover.
Step 7: Put the pillows back on the bed, one on either sidc of the bed.
Step 8: Check and adjust as needed.
Step 9: Tell yourself what a great job you did.

The steps may vary depending on the type of bed or linen. For example, if a bedspread was used an additional four steps would be needed.

The steps are taught sequentially and then combined using either a *forward or backward chaining* procedure. When using forward chaining, the initial step (or link) in the chain is taught first, then the second step is taught and then combined with the first step. The chain continues to grow until all steps are linked. Conversely, in backward chaining the last step or link is taught first, then the second to the last step is taught and linked to the last step until the entire task has been learned. The choice of which chaining procedure to use depends on the type of task and the individual being taught.

A variety of other skills can be taught by using a task analysis approach. For example, Cautela and Groden (1978) taught a modified relaxation procedure by sequentially teaching individuals with developmental disabilities to tense and relax a series of muscle groups. The steps consisted of the following:

Step 1. Sit in a relaxed position for 5 seconds.
Step 2. Tighten and relax each arm by making a fist or holding arm out straight.
Step 3. Make a fist and relax.
Step 4. Tighten and relax each leg.
Step 5. Deep breathing.

Steps 2, 3, and 4 are taught in succession by teaching the person to focus on the first muscle group, tense it on request, maintain the tension for 5-7 seconds, then release the tension and note the state of relaxation.

A task analysis can also be helpful in organizing a self-management program. Mr. Peter's program illustrates this:

Mr. Peters had difficulty in riding the bus. He often talked to strangers inappropriately, got on the wrong bus, forgot to ask for transfers when getting on the bus, and asked people to move so he could sit in his favorite seat. He had become so disruptive that the bus driver wanted him removed from the bus unless his behavior changed. The staff decided to assist Mr. Peters to learn appropriate bus riding behavior by developing a step by step outline that he could follow and check off when completed. At first, staff went with him and prompted him to identify if he had completed the step appropriately and to provide reinforcement. Mr. Peters soon was able to self-monitor his own checklist and later bring it to staff for supportive feedback.

The steps developed were as follows:

1. I stood by the bus stop.
2. I ignored strangers at the bus stop.
3. I knew my bus.
4. I waited until my bus stopped.
5. I walked up the stairs.
6. I put money in slot or showed my ID card to driver.
7. I asked for transfer.
8. I walked to empty seat and sat down or stood holding the handbars.
9. I ignored strangers on the bus.
10. I rang bell when I wanted to get off the bus.
11. I sat down until the bus stopped.
12. I walked to the closest door.
13. I waited for the door to open or pushed open door.
14. I stepped down the stairs.

For individuals with limited reading skills, the task analysis of a skill can be presented using picture cues (e.g., pictures depicting the steps of bedmaking) or even using autiotaped cues (e.g., a tape guiding the person through the relaxation steps). The following example demonstrates the use of these:

Mr. Jean Paul had an acquired head injury that severely affected his memory. He was provided a care aid to help him dress and get ready for work in the morning. However, Jean would get very angry with someone reminding him what to do. He became so difficult and aggressive that the care aids refused to provide him with support. It was decided that Mr. Paul could be independent if he could remember the steps to complete the morning routine. The staff taught him to independently follow the steps by breaking the steps down into small units, then providing him with a picture list of the steps to follow. He was taught to check off each step when it was completed. To help with this, a videotape was developed of Mr. Paul completing all the steps independently. As an initial activity in the morning, he watched the video of himself completing the morning routine successfully. More complicated steps were then broken down even further (e.g., washing was broken down into ten steps that were pictorially cued on his bathroom wall). Within only a few weeks, Jean was able to complete the steps independently to an adequate degree. By teaching him independence in these areas, the need for the aid was eliminated as were the aggressive outbursts.

Step Five: Teach Generalization

Often staff will express frustration that a person does not use new replacement skill outside the training sessions or in new situations or with new people. Staff report: *" I know he knows what he is supposed to do when he goes to the store. We discussed it. We practiced it. I reinforced him when he role played it with me. He can even tell me exactly what he is going to do. But then when he is in the situation he just doesn't do it.*" In most instances, this does not reflect a refusal to use skills but a problem with generalization. Persons with developmental disabilities often have difficulty generalizing the use of a new skill to different situations, with different people, or when the context or contingencies are somewhat different.

Research has shown that this problem can be overcome by teaching generalization during skills training. This is accomplished by:

- *training either in the natural environment where the behavior will be needed or in an environment as similar to the natural environment as possible,*

- *training provided by multiple instructors,*

- *training that include multiple examples both of the skill being taught and the circumstances where the skill might be used, and*

- *training that teaches both discrete skills (e.g., shake hands when you greet someone), and a range of skills (e.g. you hug your mother, you say hello to neighbors and you shake hands when being introduced) as well as the decision making or problem solving skills to know what skill to use in specific situations.*

Let's examine an earlier discussed example of a man going to the store. He may have been taught how to go into the store, to ask for a certain item, and to give the cashier the correct change. But does he know what to do if the desired item is not available, or if the storekeeper does not understand him, or if he has to wait while many others are served, or if the item has increased in price? Any change in the scripted learning, unless a variety of situations have been practiced, could result in the individual being unable to use his newly learned behavior. As a result, he may revert to his challenging behavior to get what he wants.

Generalization of social skills presents a particular difficult challenge. Researchers and practitioners frequently have found that, using the approaches described in this chapter, persons with developmental disabilities can learn discrete social skills. Often these skills are not used appropriately by the person when needed in the natural environment. Recent research has shown generalization depends upon (a) the relevance of the behavior, (b) the use of different teaching and generalization strategies during instruction, and (c) the continuation of reinforcement in the natural environment (Griffiths, Feldman, & Tough, 1997). See Appendix A for a description of a sample social skills training program.

Step Six: Provide Effective Reinforcement

When teaching a skill, the use of liberal reinforcement is important. However, after the skill is learned, it often is expected that the behavior should continue without reinforcement or with reinforcement naturally available in the environment. If the behavior is a valued one that will be naturally reinforced through praise, social or tangible rewards, the behavior will likely be maintained after training. For example, teaching someone a social skill that will bring about positive social contact may be naturally self-reinforcing. Or teaching a self care skill that results in increased independence may be naturally self-reinforcing. However, for some behaviors, it may be necessary to arrange the environment to insure ongoing access to reinforcement following training.

Let's see how the staff of one agency set up a creative program for Ms. Polly Turkel to reinforce her behavior on an ongoing basis. Ms. Turkel had difficulty completing her daily chores and became very angry when prompted by staff. However, without prompting to complete her least favorite tasks, she would be late for work, outings, and even meals. Staff worked out the following schedule with Polly:

- She listed the tasks that she liked to do, and staff confirmed that she generally completed these tasks without prompting.

- She also listed the tasks that she did not like. Some of these tasks were exchanged with other residents for tasks she liked to do (the other residents also agreed to this exchange). However, some disliked tasks such as her personal care remained.

- She next identified the activities that were really important to her (such as shopping, bowling, going to the coffee shop and watching her daily soap opera).

Using this information, the staff and Ms. Turkel worked out a schedule that would motivate Ms. Turkel to complete her tasks. Less desired tasks were followed by preferred tasks, thereby setting up natural reinforcement for completion of the less desired tasks. Completion of a series of tasks was followed by a desired activity such as her TV show or going out. In this way, the flow of her routine provided an ongoing schedule of reinforcement that reinforced the behavior naturally.

In the previous chapter, the reader was cautioned that unless new replacement behaviors are as effective as the inappropriate behavior in bringing about the desired positive or negative reinforcement, these behaviors may not be used. When the new behavior fails to achieve the same results at equal or greater the rate or intensity as the inappropriate behavior does, it is likely the person will use the problem behavior to gain the desired outcome.

The following provides an example of this relationship:

Miss Viola Schmidt had been taught to use prosocial communication skills to let staff know when she would like to avoid or delay an undesired task. She had been doing quite well at requesting changes rather than using disruptive behavior. The group home experienced a number of staff changes and unfortunately the staff had not been advised of Miss Schmidt's program. When she appropriately asked to do dishes at a later time so she could watch her favorite TV show, staff refused her request. She was informed "It is your night for dishes and I don't like to see dirty dishes around." Miss Schmidt repeated her request saying that she would do the dishes in an hour. The staff again refused. Miss Schmidt then began to throw things and break dishes. She was sent to her room where she watched her TV program and the staff member did the dishes and cleaned up the mess.

This example demonstrates that if the new prosocial behavior is not as effective at bringing about the desired negative or positive reinforcement as the inappropriate behavior has been, the individual likely will use the more effective challenging behavior. To summarize, successful maintenance of a replacement skill depends on the effectiveness of the behavior in bringing about the desired outcome. A common reason for replacement skill program failure is that the new behavior is not as effective as the challenging behavior in producing positive or negative reinforcement.

In environments that do not offer natural reinforcement for new skills, it is important to teach individuals in the environment to routinely offer reinforcement for prosocial skills. Some environments do not provide appropriate levels of natural reinforcement to maintain prosocial behaviors. When this occurs, it can be concluded that an habilitatively appropriate environment is not present. The nature of the environment, not the individual, becomes the target of intervention.

Step Seven: Remove Reinforcement For The Challenging Behaviors

Teaching replacement skill and establishing their effectiveness as alternatives to challenging behaviors is only one component of the treatment plan. The second component is designed to reduce the effectiveness of the problem behavior. Why should a person learn a new behavior if the challenging behavior is working? If the reinforcement value of the new behavior is to be greater, it is important to respond differently to the challenging behavior.

Challenging behaviors exist because these work in bringing about desired outcomes. It may have resulted in reinforcement every time or perhaps only on some occasions. But these do bring about the desired positive or negative reinforcement. Once the new skill has been taught and results in reinforcement, it is critical to remove the reinforcement for the challenging behavior.

Let's take an example:

Mr. Paulson had the challenging behavior of screaming. He would scream whenever he wanted out of an unpleasant situation. The staff could not cope with his screaming and would send him to his room. The behavior had been quite effective for a number of years as a way of escaping undesired activities. The group home staff providing Mr. Paulson with a communication board so that he could make his wishes known. When he wanted out of a situation he was taught to press the "stop" button on his board. An automated voice would then say, "I want to stop this now." Staff would reinforce Mr. Paulson with praise for using his button and allow him to leave the task or go to his room as he wished. This was working about 50% of the time. However, the rest of the time, Mr. Paulson still screamed to escape the situation.

The other 50% of the time, the staff used a planned ignoring procedure. When Mr. Paulson began to scream, the staff would remind him to use his board if he wanted to stop the task. The staff continued the task and ignored his screaming until he either stopped screaming, at which time they gave a second reminder to use his button, or until he pressed the appropriate button. He was then praised for using his stop button and allowed to discontinue the task.

Step Eight: Collect Data For Evaluation And Decision Making

Any intervention should be monitored for success. Our perceptions and memories can be very misleading.

Let's examine the following example:

> Miss Mary Buggle was working with a young woman who was very negative and aggressive. She began reinforcing the woman for using more appropriate and polite ways of addressing her. After two weeks, she reported that the behavior problems were greatly improved. Analysis of data taken independently by another staff member revealed no difference in the aggressive behavior, even though she had shown improvement in polite ways of addressing staff.

As a second example:

> Ms. Patricia Smiley was teaching a man an alternative way of getting out of undesired household tasks. The man had been using destructive behaviors as his means of gaining escape. After a month, Patricia announced the program had failed. However, data obtained by an observer demonstrated a significant change. The number and intensity of the outbursts had reduced by 50% in that month.

Why were the staff perceptions or memories unable to accurately reflect what was happening in these situations? Although many reasons may result in biased perceptions or memories about challenging behavior, a major reason is that there are often many competing and demanding job related activities which may interfere with the accuracy of observations.

Traditionally, data are collected only on the person's challenging behavior. While this is important and reinforcing for staff, it also is equally important to record changes in the replacement skill. If a prosocial skill is replacing the problem behavior, there should be an inverse change in the challenging behavior and the replacement behavior.

Who should collect data?

Data can be collected either by staff or the person receiving the instruction. Some benefits occur whenever staff keep the data. Staff can be monitoring the progress as it happens so that changes in the program can be made as needed. Also, if staff maintain and analyze data regularly, greater program consistency and follow through may occur.

Record keeping by the learner also has some advantages. It often is reinforcing and helps the person to self-evaluate and self-monitor. A combination of both the staff and the learner might be optimal.

How often should data be collected?

The data collection schedule should be kept as simple as possible. Otherwise it will interfere with ongoing activities and learning and likely will be neglected. As it is recommended that training occur in the natural environment (e.g., in the store, on the bus, or in the work setting), it would be most inappropriate for staff to be following people around with a clipboard checking off the steps of task analysis. Develop a natural and simple method to record the changing behaviors.

Conclusion

The teaching of competency skills as replacements for challenging behaviors represents a central strategy of *Individual Centred Behavioral Interventions*. This Chapter provided a series of program suggestions for ensuring that replacement competencies are acquired and do gain dominance over challenging behaviors.

CHAPTER TEN

RESPONDING TO ESCALATING PROBLEMS

Dorothy M. Griffiths and Jo Anne Nugent

In this chapter, we discuss one of the more perplexing and difficult issues in behavioral programming—dealing with crisis.

Sometimes, in spite of all our planning and related intervention efforts, an individual's challenging behaviors seem to escalate in frequency and severity until it becomes dangerous to self and others. As caregivers, we resort to tactics that get us through the situation as safely as possible. Then we sit down and try to figure out what happened and how we can prevent it from happening again!

Individual Centered Behavioral Interventions is a positive approach. A consistent use of *Individual Centered Behavioral Interventions* to support individuals who experience frequent crisis can be effective in the long run with continued use of positive interventions. If behavior containment procedures become necessary to protect the person and others, those procedures are individually selected to represent the least intrusive and disruptive to the individual. At the same time, these offer the greatest likelihood of terminating the current out-of-control episode in the shortest time possible.

What Typically Happens During Crisis?

When we talk about crisis in behavioral terms, we are referring to a situation in which an individual's behavior is dangerous, threatening or highly disruptive to the individual and others (Griffiths, 1989). In a sense, the person has lost personal control of his/her actions and needs some immediate assistance from others in order to regain self-control. Typical examples include:

*   *serious* self abuse such as head banging,
*   *violent* aggression against others, and
*   *destruction* of property.

These behaviors frighten us.

The seriousness of the situation may panic us to the extent that common sense or planned programs fly out the window.

Our priority during a crisis is always safety. Unfortunately, to protect everyone involved, we too quickly and too often resort to routine use of behavior containment methods without any attempts to use other behavioral management procedures that may avoid an out-of-control crisis. Methods often used include: physical restraint such as holding, isolation, or mechanical devices and/or chemical restraint (Gardner & Sovner, 1994). While these containment procedures may be required on occasion to protect the person and/or others from harm, when used excessively or as a routine approach to out-of-control behaviors, these become inappropriate and violate the basic premise of our positive individual centered philosophy. Categorical use of behavior containment methods may serve the purpose of getting everyone through the crisis with less damage, but the long-term benefits are negative.

What's Wrong With Excessive Reliance On Behavior Containment During Crisis?

Exclusive or excessive dependence on behavior containment procedures during crisis situations is inconsistent with our individual centered perspective. Some reasons why using this approach is not recommended include the following.

Behavior Containment May Violate Personal Autonomy and Individual Dignity

When staff exert control, individuals lose control. This contradicts our ethics and our sense of human rights. Not only is the individual's personal autonomy comprised, but the individual's dignity is diminished. There is nothing dignified about being physically restrained or physically escorted out of a room kicking and screaming, even though these procedures occasionally may be necessary to insure the safety of the person or others.

Our ultimate goal is to support the person in developing personal control. Therefore, we attempt to minimize or eliminate behavior containment procedures and, when needed, to include these in an intervention plan that maximizes personal control.

Behavior Containment Does Not Solve The Problem

Excessive use of behavior containment procedures is like a Band-Aid. It may protect the person and others in the immediate situation, but does not get to the root of the problem.

As we have seen, behaviors are caused by a multitude of factors. We must develop a complete intervention plan to deal with these multiple factors if we are to make any meaningful impact on the challenging behavior. Otherwise, we are doomed to a cycle of crisis ⇨ behavior containment ⇨ crisis ⇨ behavior containment that goes on indefinitely.

To influence the challenging behaviors to the extent that behavior containment procedures become rare or are no longer needed, we must follow the Case Formulation Process and provide *person specific* proactive behavioral supports.

Behavior Containment Procedures May Make The Situation Worse

Sometimes, behavior containment methods may have the unintended effect of making the behavior worse (Gardner & Sovner, 1994). This is usually related to the consequences produced by the containment procedure. For example, an individual usually receives increased staff attention when violent behavior occurs. This attention may be reinforcing for the individual who quickly learns that the best way to get more attention is to be violent again. Likewise, an individual may enjoy the physical contact involved in being restrained. Additionally, the challenging behavior might serve an avoidance *function* if the individual is removed from an aversive environment. Other people may find being placed in isolation a relaxing experience and may deliberately act in ways that guarantee prompt removal to the isolation location!

In summary, in using behavior containment methods to reactively manage crises, we may have the unintended effect of increasing the number and intensity of the crises as the containment procedures may contain elements of reinforcement.

This brings us back to our question of why the behavior occurs. Answers to this question provide direction to proactive interventions that remove the basis for the crisis producing behaviors.

Excessive Use Of Behavior Containment Procedures Destroys The Individual/Staff Relationship

In Chapter Eight we discussed how important rapport is to the teaching situation. Nothing destroys rapport more quickly than repeated situations in which one adult is restraining the other adult. How can we expect individuals to respond positively to staff trying to teach them new skills when these same staff have recently restrained them or physically escorted them to an isolation area?

Excessive and inappropriate use of behavior containment procedures negatively impacts on our long term success in teaching the individual new skills of coping with the crisis producing antecedents. Under these conditions, our positive approach is compromised.

Staff Feel Terrible

Most of us enter human services to offer valuable support for others. We do not choose to work with people with developmental disabilities in order to exert control over their lives. One often over looked aspect of excessive use of behavior containment procedures is that there is a tremendous cost to staff. In a sense, staff are punished too. They feel badly about themselves. This leads to their becoming less effective in providing habilitatively appropriate experiences. They eventually may not even want to work with a person because his/her crisis behaviors constantly put them in a position of using procedures that causes them discomfort.

High staff morale and positive attitudes are crucial elements of working successfully with persons who have developmental disabilities and challenging behaviors.

Using *Individual Centered Behavioral Interventions*

Let's now examine how we can use *Individual Centered Behavioral Interventions* to deal effectively with escalating behaviors and crisis. There are six steps to this process.

Prevent Through Assessment

If we observe that behavior is escalating and in danger of reaching crisis proportions, we should immediately evaluate the situation to determine what is contributing to the escalating behaviors. If the immediate reasons for the escalation are evident, attempt to remove or minimize these and redirect the person into alternative activities. If we understand what precipitated the crisis, proactive approaches can be initiated to avoid its recurrence.

Our immediate objective is to prevent the crisis from happening. However, *it is important that we do not abandon our current intervention plan if a crisis does occur!* The current plan often remains valid, but other factors may have entered into the picture. We need to identify what these other factors are. A crisis can be discouraging. Everyone may be quite pleased because things are going well and the individual centered interventions are working.

Then, crisis occurs! By assessing what produced the crisis, we may be able to get "back on track."

Perhaps circumstances have changed. Perhaps the individual is experiencing new *vulnerabilities and related instigating influences* such as illness. Perhaps other new *instigating* factors have appeared or old ones have reappeared. It could be that consequences for prosocial behavior are no longer present. Changes in staff or environments, appearance or exacerbation of physical or mental illness symptoms, and a range of other antecedent changes may be impacting on the effectiveness of our interventions. It is quite possible that approaches contained in the person's intervention plan are not being implemented consistently or appropriately.

In any event, a diligent attempt should be made to discover what is happening now to cause the crisis. Above all, we should not give up on positive approaches or on the person.

Give The Person A Holiday

In some instances, it may be feasible to give the person a holiday from his/her general program routine. This does not mean that we send the individual to Bermuda! What this does mean is that we remove the person from potential and known *instigating* factors relating to the crisis behaviors. If a person is provoked to violent or dangerous behaviors that become out-of-control, insure that the instigating conditions are avoided. If someone's behavior starts to escalate, interrupt it early, redirect him/her or remove him/her from the source of agitation.

At the same time, we can elevate reinforcement levels, both on a noncontingent basis and for a range of appropriate behaviors. This may create a more general positive mood state that in turn (a) serves as an instigating condition for a range of prosocial coping behaviors and (b) competes with negative emotional arousal that frequently accompany crisis behaviors.

In other words, we make the environment as pleasant and stress free as possible for the individual. These are *transition* strategies. Certainly, these will provide a "breather" during which the person can have positive experience and we can calmly revise the intervention plan to address the instigating conditions associated with the crisis episode.

Protect The Person And Others In The Environment

Our first priority during an out-of-control episode remains that of protection of the individual and others. We want to avoid injury or significant property destruction. Therefore, we may use behavior containment procedures in out-of-control episodes that pose a danger to self or others. Even in such circumstances, we can attempt to decrease the potential negative impact of the behavior containment techniques used. Procedures should be selected based on features of the person in crisis. Physical holding one person who is harming himself may assist in his regaining control quickly while this same procedure used with another person may merely intensify that person's agitation.

Whenever the situation permits, we should attempt less intrusive behavior management procedures prior to using behavior containment methods. Perhaps one particular staff has better luck verbally directing an individual who is escalating to an isolation or calming area rather than using physical escort. Whenever possible, use that staff member to provide any needed crisis management.

To protect the dignity of the person when behavior containment procedures become necessary, if the situation permits we may clear the room of onlookers before we restrain someone. The procedure results in less embarrassment to the person being restrained and is less emotionally disruptive to others.

Revise Intervention Plan As Needed

We may modify the existing intervention plan as needed to reflect new assessment information. In some instances, the original plan may be quite appropriate but has not been used consistently or appropriately. In this instance, staff training and commitment to using the plan are needed.

Emphasize Positive Interventions

A person who presents repeated out-of-control episodes experiences considerable negative emotional arousal. These must be offset with numerous positive emotional experiences. Following crisis episodes, it is essential that frequent positive program experiences be provided on a regular basis. The person's intervention plan may need monitoring on an ongoing basis to insure that this is occurring.

Chances are that serious behavior problems resulting in crisis episodes will require several reassessments and revisions to the person's behavioral support plan. We may still have the wrong hypotheses. We may have partially correct hypotheses. Perhaps circumstances will change again and we will be required to update our *Individual Centered Behavioral Intervention* plan on several occasions.

Develop An Individual Centered Crisis Intervention Plan

As discussed earlier, the intervention plan of an individual with a history of out-of-control behaviors addresses in detail those individually selected procedures to follow whenever a crisis occurs. This crisis intervention component of the person's multimodal behavior intervention plan is basically a description of who will do what the next time there is a crisis. As noted, these procedures represent approaches to follow after other less intrusive proactive and reactive behavior management procedures have been ineffective in terminating or decreasing the person's escalation. Experience has taught us that even the best proactive treatment and management strategies will not immediately eliminate serious behavior problems of those individuals who are experiencing ongoing crises. Thus, well defined and individually designed crisis intervention procedures become an essential therapeutic component of the support plan.

To emphasize, these crisis intervention procedures are individually tailored and as positive and minimally intrusive as possible. It should also be clear to everyone that this crisis intervention component is only for emergencies and that use of these will decrease over time as our proactive positive interventions take effect.

Summary

As a crisis plan is developed, review the process by which decisions were made. Have the following steps been followed to ensure that a comprehensive individual centered plan has been developed?

Step 1: What is the challenging behavior and does the behavior warrant intervention?

Step 2: Has diagnostic information been gathered on biomedical, psychological, and socioenvironmental conditions that could be contributing to the behavior?

Step 3: Have assessment findings resulted in diagnostic hypotheses?

Step 4: Have specific program objectives been identified relative to the causes outlined in Step 3?

Step 5: Has a set of intervention formulations been developed that addresses the hypothesized causes of the challenging behavior?

Step 6: Has an integrated set of individual centered interventions based on specific diagnostic-intervention formulations been selected?

Step 7: Has a staging plan been developed to introduce the various interventions?

Step 8: Has an evaluation process been developed to measure the effectiveness of the interventions on both the challenging and replacement behaviors?

Step 9: Are changes made to the intervention plan based on evaluation results?

These quality assurance guidelines are summarized in Appendix C.

Conclusion

Dealing with escalating behaviors and crises may appear to be
overwhelming! However, once we have managed a crisis successfully, it is important to review the proactive treatment and
management components of the person's intervention plan. Crises do not represent a failure but rather provides a signal to us to
rethink what is happening, and to act on our analysis.

Above all, it is important to reaffirm the value of the positive
behavioral approach!

CHAPTER ELEVEN

CREATING AN INTEGRATED SERVICE SYSTEM

Dorothy M. Griffiths and Jo Anne Nugent

The multimodal (bio-psycho-social) perspective was introduced in Chapter Two to guide us in gaining an understanding of the "why" of challenging behaviors. This perspective suggests that best understanding occurs when consideration is given to the possible roles of biomedical, psychological and socioenvironmental influences. We also suggested that a variety of factors typically are involved in the chronic occurrence of challenging behaviors for persons with development disabilities who also have significant mental health concerns. For any challenging behavior, consideration is given to the possible instigating, vulnerability, and reinforcing roles served by biomedical, psychological, and socioenvironmental features.

Once hypotheses are formed about why specific challenging behaviors are occurring, we select those interventions based on diagnostic formulations that offer best hope of changing the behavioral challenges in a way that will improve the person's quality of life. If the reasons for a person's challenging behaviors encompass several aspects of his/her life, interventions are selected to address each of these. This typically involves services from a variety of professionals. The *Individual Centered Behav-*

ioral Interventions approach requires this integrated multimodal (bio-psycho-social) contextual (instigating, vulnerability, and reinforcing) perspective.

Unfortunately, this multimodal perspective involving a variety of persons working together on a common behavioral support plan often is missing in service delivery for persons with challenging behaviors. Instead, the following models characterize how services too frequently are delivered.

Model 1: Partializing

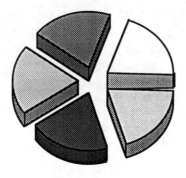

In *Model 1*, the individual is assessed by a variety of different agencies, services, and individual professionals with each group or person determining how to handle the part of the individual's life that they are trained or mandated to serve. The psychiatrist deals with the person's aberrant moods and contact with reality. The psychologist and behavior analyst assess cognitive, personality, motivation, emotions and conduct a behavior analysis. The vocational instructor plans the work activities. The residential manager plans for "a bed." It is readily apparent that the person is separated into a number of individual components with no one looking at the person as a whole. This is referred to as *partializing*.

Model 2: Problem Intensification

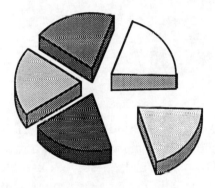

If one or more problems become acute (as examples, the challenging behavior escalates or the psychiatric illness such as depression dramatically changes), the entire system shifts to emphasize that part of the individual that seems to be most problematic at the moment. The person loses his/her identity as a whole person and becomes known as the "aggressive one," or the "self injurious behavior case," or the "schizophrenic." In this *problem intensification model*, systems get distorted in response to specific "crisis" problems. Usually, medications get increased, behavior programs become more intense and restrictive, and the person's lifestyle becomes distorted. At this point, the person's entire daily routine is focused on "the problem" and how to manage it.

Model 3: Systems Exclusion

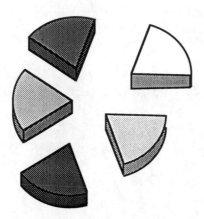

As problems escalate, the individual parts of the service system begin to exclude the individual from services and eventually from the community. The person is deemed, for example, as a community failure, a placement failure, or a treatment failure. The person becomes a victim of *systems exclusion.*

Seamless Service System

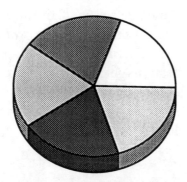

In contrast to these three models of service delivery involving *partializing, problem intensification and systems exclusion* is a model in which systems work together to understand the individual in his/her entirety. All facets of the individual interact and so should all parts of the system. The system must be intact and openly interactive if the individual is to receive individual centered services.

Services provided Mr. Joe Perot, a young man with severe cognitive impairment, provides an example of a *seamless service delivery system.*

Mr. Perot occasionally becomes highly aggressive with staff when taken to a doctor's office for a scheduled appointment. Assessment reveals that, although Mr. Perot on every doctor's appointment demonstrates numerous signs of fearfulness, he usually can be encouraged to keep these appointments. During periods of time in the spring and fall, however, he becomes increasingly resistive and becomes aggressive if prompted to keep the appointment. In fact, assessment reveals that Joe is generally more disruptive and unhappy during these periods of the year. Medical tests revealed seasonal allergies. We thus hypothesized that both Mr. Perot's long-standing fear of doctor appointments and his allergies represent personal *vulnerability* conditions. When his allergies are active, Mr. Perot is more likely to display challenging behavioral episodes. The psychological distress level produced by the allergies plus his anxiety arousal associated with the doctor's appointment (both contributing conditions) combine with staff prompts for him to go for his appointment (the triggering event) to *instigate* the aggressive acts. We also hypothesized that his aggression is *functional* as these acts occasionally are reinforced by his being able to avoid or delay the doctor's appointment. Finally, lack of anxiety management skills and skills of adequately communicating his fearfulness represent additional psychological vulnerabilities.

Our interventions would focus on each of these areas presumed to be contributing to the instigation, chronic recurrence, and reinforcement of Mr. Perot's challenging behaviors. These would involve medical treatment of the allergies, emotional desensitization to reduce the fear of doctors appointments, skills of coping with "normal" levels of anxiety surrounding medical treatment, and communication skills training to provide means of sharing his concerns without resorting to aggression. Each of these interventions would involve the participation of care givers such as residential staff who would be obtaining and administering medication for allergies, assisting with behavioral supports, and providing communication training.

As illustrated in this example, it is crucial that interventions address each of the hypothesized influences in an integrated manner. To accomplish this, a team of people providing specific services to address those issues related to areas of expertise. If we attempt to provide treatment on a piecemeal basis, effectiveness will be diminished.

Inclusive treatment requires the involvement of all relevant people. This is what we mean by the term *"seamless service system."* The individual needs relevant professionals who can meet the person's needs to work together in a coordinated way to provide the range of necessary interventions. This *multidisciplinary team* representing specialized backgrounds is of especial importance in working with a person with a developmental disability with severely challenging behaviors This is crucial as the factors contributing to the problem frequently involve biomedical, psychological, and environmental conditions.

Although a multidisciplinary integrated approach seems so sensible, we all have experienced the frustrations of attempting to provide services to someone in a coordinated way. As described earlier as Model 1: Partializing, far too often the individual's needs are divided into pieces. Each professional takes one piece to deal with, and does not communicate with the other professionals who are involved.

How can we create a seamless service system in order to provide the best possible supports for our individuals? The following discussion offers some strategies to creating such a system.

Defining A Seamless Service System

Let's begin by defining what we mean by the concept *"seamless service system."*

A seamless service system is:

A collection of professionals who work together in a coordinated way to develop a holistic behavior support plan and to insure that services are delivered according to this plan for the purposes of best meeting all the needs of the individual.

The key concepts in this definition are:

- *collection of professionals*—we need a range of professionals available when required for assessment and treatment of the various bio-psycho-social conditions that may influence challenging behaviors.

- *coordinated*—assessment and interventions should be provided in an organized, cooperative manner.

- *holistic behavior supports plan*—a plan of supports should be developed which deals with the individual as a total human being, while recognizing his/her needs in those areas of life that influence the challenging behaviors.

- *insure*—the seamless system should be organized so that all identified needs are met and the individual does not "fall between the cracks" if some of these needs are atypical, costly, or require cross sector collaboration

- *meeting the needs of the individual*—this represents our major purpose for management and treatment efforts provided by members of the team.

Linking this all together is clear communication. We recognize that clear and frequent communication is the key to a *seamless service system.* We must insure that we share all information in a format that is understandable to all participants.

The Core Value Of Treatment

When any group of people come together to carry out any activity, they must share some sense of common goals or purpose in order to succeed. This does not imply that these people must agree on every issue or topic. However, a fundamental agreement is needed concerning the overall reason for working together.

> Think about staff in a group home working with a young woman who present challenging behaviors. Each staff member will have a different personal style and manner of relating to that woman. However, all staff must pursue common goals with regards to her. For example, one goal of the individual plan might be to provide maximum community integration in order to improve the woman's quality of life. Each staff might have different responsibilities in supporting her in reaching this goal. One staff member may support her to attend a cooking class, while another staff teaches her independent transit skills. Yet the goal, and its underlying value, are shared by all.

Similarly, our multidisciplinary team members will provide different services according to their expertise. The members nonetheless must share a key core value to work together to insure successful treatment. A *seamless service system* is founded on sharing a core value.

Individual Centered Goals Should Guide The Intervention Program

As discussed in previous chapters, far too often program goals are developed to meet the needs of everyone but the individual. This is particularly evident with persons with developmental disabilities and significant challenging behaviors. These behaviors can create considerable disruption and stress for caregivers. The intervention plan often consists of approaches aimed at eliminating the problem behavior to the caregiver's benefit, but with inadequate consideration of the person's needs as voiced by him or her.

If members of the multidisciplinary team agree that all management and treatment approaches must support the individual's goals, a common core value is shared. Sharing the same core value means that they will have the same long term vision for all intervention efforts. There may be some disagreements about some of the individual components of the plan. They will certainly perform different services for the individual. However, all team members should agree that the ultimate purpose for treatment is quality of life for the individual, as defined from the individual's point of view.

Strategies To Develop A Seamless Service System

The following represent strategies that may be useful in development of a *seamless service system.*

Strategy 1: Designate A Coordinator

Someone must assume the role of organizing all the required

professionals into a team. This person will be responsible for ensuring that the coordinated development and delivery of the treatment plan takes place—the *seamless* element.

This role includes making sure that basic practical steps such as arranging meetings, inviting the necessary people, chairing meetings, preparing minutes, and maintaining ongoing communication are carried out. In some situations, this may mean that the coordinator assumes all these duties. In other situations, the coordinator will arrange for others to share the duties.

Another crucial component of this role is to confirm that the core value is agreed to and upheld by all participants. To insure adherence, the coordinator routinely monitors the service delivery process to insure that the individual's goals are the focus of all interventions. To accomplish this, the coordinator must understand the individual well enough to be familiar with the person's goals.

The coordinator is also responsible for monitoring the service delivery process to ensure that none of the needs is being ignored or overlooked. If unmet needs are detected, the coordinator should immediately bring this to the attention of the multidisciplinary team.

As can be imagined, the role of coordinator requires certain skills. The person must be an excellent communicator, be diplomatic, and be persistent. If the coordinator behaves in a fair and dignified manner, he/she will earn the respect and cooperation of the professionals involved.

The person who serves as coordinator will vary from situation to situation.

Sometimes, a staff person is specifically hired to be a "case manager" or a "case coordinator." If a funded case manager is not available, a staff member such as a primary residential counselor, a vocational staff, or a social worker may assume the coordinator's role. Sometimes, a parent may assume the coordinator role. The person's job title is not as important as the person's skills and commitment to the individual.

In summary, the coordinator plays a key role in organizing and maintaining the multidisciplinary team. Without someone assuming this role, it is unlikely that services will be delivered in a *seamless* way.

Strategy 2: Involve All Relevant People On The Team

The team should be as complete as possible. We then can insure that all factors that contribute to the behavior will be identified and addressed. Each professional providing services to the individual should be part of the team. Others who have a personal interest in the individual, such as family or friends, may also be included in team consideration.

Usually, the team conducts its business through meetings. The coordinator assumes the responsibility of inviting all relevant parties to the initial meeting. At this meeting, participants may suggest others who can be invited to expand the team. Indeed, people may join the team throughout the process if new areas of service need are discovered.

Team participation does not always involve attendance at every meeting. Professionals have very busy schedules and may not be able to come to all or any meetings. However, even if someone cannot attend, that person can still participate by regularly communicating with the team. Usually, the coordinator is responsible for insuring that information from those who cannot attend is available at meetings. As well, the coordinator communicates back to those who cannot attend about the results of the meetings.

It is ideal if all the key players can indeed attend meetings. However, if this cannot happen, the coordinator has the important job of insuring that all relevant people work together effectively.

Strategy 3: Respect the Contributions of All Team Members

To insure that the team works well together, all members should view themselves as valued team members. One important ingredient of a *seamless service system* is that all participants *honor* and respect each other.

Everyone comes to the team with useful expertise and important information. Such expertise and information may be needed to develop the best possible intervention program. Sometimes, key information needed to understand someone's behavior comes from the person who supports the individual on a daily basis. That person may provide valued information that no one else has.

When professionals from different disciplines comprise the team, some members may find it difficult to respect the training and expertise of staff from disciplines different from their own. A status game may be played. Some professionals with more education or a higher salary may want to control team decisions. They may find it difficult to participate on a team in which power is shared.

Some team members may be "nonprofessionals" such as family members or advocates. These participants offer unique information and a personal dedication to the individual which is usually not matched by any professional. As a result, they are essential participants.

Finally, in all but exceptional situations, the individual presenting the challenging behaviors should attend meetings of the team. We should be particularly careful to be supportive of an individual's attempts to participate since the individual may find the meeting to be somewhat overwhelming. After all, our purpose is to be of assistance to the person served. We must make all reasonable efforts to support that person to be a meaningful part of the process of providing high quality services to him/her.

How can we ensure that all participants on our team are indeed valued? It is the job of the chairperson at meetings to continually solicit input from all participants. The chairperson also models appropriate respect for all who attend and redirects interactions that violate this respect. Other team members also share the responsibility of treating each other with consideration.

By honoring all participants, we can build a team which works cooperatively towards a common goal.

Strategy 4: Begin By Learning The Individual's Personal Goals

We have suggested that our services should assist the individual to accomplish his/her own goals. Our focus should be to improve the individual's quality of life. To establish the importance of this, it is useful to begin the program development process by learning what the individual's goals are.

We therefore initiate the planning process in a positive way and reinforce our core value. The individual tells us what his/her hopes and dreams are. This gives all team members a vision for the future. Imagine how much more inspiring this is than the usual meeting format which begins with a long listing of all the individual's problems. By the time the listing is done, everyone feels hopeless and all our creative energies are gone. We cannot see past the problems to find the person.

An initial focus on the individual's goals also provides guidelines for the intervention plan. When we plan an intervention, we can ask ourselves "Will this assist the person to accomplish his/her goals?" If the answer is "NO," we should rethink our intervention.

Sometimes, professionals listen to an individual's goals with a cynical attitude. We have been trained to look for people's deficiencies. If a man with severely challenging problems tells us that he wants to live independently in his own apartment, we quickly respond with several reasons why this cannot be. Usually, the reasons focus on his inadequacies—he is aggressive, he cannot cook, he will not carry out his hygiene routines, he cannot use a telephone, and so on. However, it is our job as professionals to support him to maximize his own skills and to provide assistance in supplementing these. We must look beyond the deficiencies to see the strengths and develop strategies to deal effectively with these current limitations.

This can be accomplished most effectively if the individual is attending the planning meetings. If not clinically advisable, people who know the individual well should be responsible for ensuring that the individual's wishes are conveyed to the team. As well, the individual should be kept informed regarding the team's plans. Not all individuals are able to communicate their goals in a clearly understandable format. Those who know the individual best may need to interpret what the person would like in his/her life based on their knowledge of the individual.

In sum, we begin our planning process with identifying the individual's goals. This initial activity reinforces our core value and focuses us on the future.

Strategy 5: Complete A Thorough Assessment

Next, we complete a thorough assessment of possible conditions influencing the challenging behaviors. Earlier chapters describe the content and process of this activity. The key point is to gather accurate information about those facets of the individual's life— biomedical, psychological, social-environmental—that appear relevant to the challenging behaviors. This information should be translated into the multimodal diagnostic format described earlier.

This format summarizes the biopsychosocial information relating to *instigating factors, vulnerabilities, and functions* relevant to the individual's challenging behavior. This integrated multimodal report highlights current information about relevant biomedical, psychological and social-environmental influences. Interventions derived from these multimodal diagnostic formulations frequently will require services from persons of various disciplines. This type of report will help everyone to understand our *seamless* approach. In other words, a thorough assessment report stresses the impact of each system. It assists all professionals to realize that effective interventions require the professional contributions of many disciplines. Therefore, team members develop an appreciation of each other's work. This eliminates the tendency of some professionals to work in isolation under the faulty belief that only their intervention is required.

Strategy 6: Develop A Comprehensive Intervention Plan

If we know the individual's goals and have a thorough assessment, we are in a position to develop a *seamless* intervention plan. The most effective plan, as noted, will be a *multimodal contextual* one which addresses relevant *instigating factors, vulnerabilities, and functions* of the challenging behavior. As emphasized, the plan should focus on the individual's goals and on improving the person's quality of life.

The treatment plan should include:

- *long term* goals,
- *short term* objectives, and
- *specific actions*, including the responsible parties and time lines.

A suitable plan is easily understood by all, including nonprofessionals. Everyone should know who is doing what and when this is to be accomplished. By ensuring that everyone knows the roles of all team members in implementing the intervention plan, a seamless service delivery system evolves.

Strategy 7: Collect Relevant Program Effectiveness Data

No one is thrilled by the task of collecting data! However, as noted in Chapter Five, a suitable monitoring system is needed to evaluate the effectiveness of various components of the overall intervention efforts. Data reflecting changes in relevant target areas are needed to evaluate the impact of various interventions and to provide support for the diagnostic formulations about contributing factors. In short, information is needed to tells us whether our hypotheses and related interventions have utility.

Relevant information about the targets of intervention also is of value in facilitating communication among professionals. Information presented in a clear manner is easily understood by others and increases the credibility of various interventions. It can become a focus of discussion which will facilitate the team meeting process. We mentioned an assessment report organized around the various classes of contributing conditions. Similarly, data should be obtained and organized to reflect the effects of modifying these presumed causes. This type of data report makes it easier for team members to understand if specific interventions designed to modify specific influences are successful.

Strategy 8: Communicate

It is crucial that team members communicate routinely and as frequently as needed to inform each other about what is being done and the impact of each. What occurs in one part of the individual's life will have an impact on all other areas. Keeping up to date is vital.

For example, a medication may be prescribed to treat a physical problem. This medication may have negative side effects on the person's behavior. All other team members should be informed about these potential side effects for two reasons. First, services can be adjusted as required to support the individual through these side effects. Second, each person will understand that the behavior changes influenced by the medication may impact other current interventions.

It also is important to communicate if nothing has changed! If a specific intervention has no effect on the challenging behaviors, team members need to know this as well.

The coordinator has responsibility for communicating relevant information to all parties. This keeps all team members interested and involved. Fortunately, in the age of answering machines and fax machines, this communication duty is not as difficult as has been true in the past.

Strategy 9: Establish A Regular Meeting Schedule

Challenging behaviors of persons with developmental disabilities typically do not disappear quickly. We can anticipate an intervention process that may take an extended period of time. It is important to maintain the sense of commitment from all participants over time. It also is important to maintain ongoing communication.

One way of insuring this is to establish a regular schedule for meetings. This schedule should be realistic as staff or consultants do not have the time to meet frequently. Yet, it is important that meetings be frequent enough to insure exchange of information in a timely way. It is also important that meetings are of sufficient frequency to maintain a sense of being a team. Those involved must establish a meeting schedule which makes sense according to the particular individual's needs.

Meeting schedules change over time. At first, meetings might be quite frequent, while the individual's goals are being established, assessments are being conducted, and diagnostic-intervention formulations are being developed. As interventions become increasingly effective, meetings usually become less frequent.

Even as time between meetings increases, ongoing communication should continue. We must insure that our *seamless service system* does not become unraveled.

Strategy 10: Celebrate Successes

This may seem like an odd statement to make when we are talking about professional treatment and service systems.

Yet, we must remember that service systems are comprised of people. People need and appreciate positive strokes! We should acknowledge and celebrate our successful efforts.

Celebration has many benefits. First, team members renew their sense of hope and enthusiasm. Second, team members are more likely to stay with a team that is appreciative. Third, team members understand the holistic approach better as they learn how positive changes occur through the combined interventions of all participants.

Conclusion

Strategies to insure a *seamless service system* have been recommended. These strategies do not work overnight. It takes time and persistence to change a large bureaucracy like human services. However, the results are well worth the efforts. A *seamless service system* is the most effective way to provide supports for person with developmental disabilities with serious behavioral challenges as a variety of factors affect these behaviors.

Selected References

Allyon, T., & Azrin, N. H. (1968). The Token Economy: A motivational system for therapy and rehabilitation. New York, NY: Appleton-Century Crofts.

Aman, M. G., Singh, N. N., Stewart, A. W., & Field, C. J. (1985). The Aberrant Behavior Checklist: A behavior rating scale for the assessment of treatment effects. American Journal of Mental Deficiency, 89, 485-491.

Bailey, J. S., & Pyles, D. A. (1989). Behavioral diagnostics. In E. Cipani (Ed), The treatment of severe behavior disorders: Behavior analysis approaches (pp. 85-107). Washington, DC: American Association on Mental Retardation.

Bambara, L. M., Mitchell-Kvacky, N. Z., & Iacobelli, S. (1994). Positive behavioral support for students with severe disabilities: An emerging multicomponent approach for addressing challenging behaviors. School Psychology Review, 23(2), 263-278.

Brown, L., Shiraga, B., York, J., Zanella, K., & Rogan, P. (1984). A life space analysis strategy for students with severe handicaps. Madison: University of Wisconsin and Madison Metropolitan School District.

Brown, M. G., Gardner, W. I., & Davidson, D. P. (1998). A setting event analysis of behavior disorders among persons with profound mental retardation. Submitted for publication.

Carr, E. G., & Durand, V. M. (1985). Reducing behavior problems through functional communication training. Journal of Applied Behavior Analysis, 18, 111-126.

Carr, E. G., McConnachie, G., Levin, L., & Kemp, D. C. (1989). Communication-based treatment of severe behavior problems. In R. Van Houten & S. Axelrod (Eds.), Effective behavioral treatment: Issues and implementation. New York, NY: Plenum.

Cautela, J. R., & Groden, J. (1978). Relaxation: A comprehensive manual for adults, children, and children with special needs. Champaign, IL: Research Press.

Coccaro, E. F. (1989). Central serotonin and impulsive aggression. British Journal of Psychiatry, 155 (suppl. 8), 52-62.

Cole, C. L., & Gardner, W. I. (1990). Effects of staff- and self-assessment procedures on disruptive behavior in a vocational setting: A case study. Vocational Evaluation and Work Adjustment Bulletin, 23, 41-46.

Cole, C. L., Gardner, W. I., & Karan, O. (1985). Self-management training of mentally retarded adults presenting severe conduct difficulties. Applied Research in Mental Retardation, 6, 337-347.

Cowan, E. L., Huser, D. R., & Rappaport, J. (1970). Parent perceptions of young children and their relation to indexes of development. Journal of Consulting and Clinical Psychology, 34, 97-103.

Donnellan, A. M., Mirenda, P. L., Mesaros, R. A., & Fassbender, L. L. (1984). Analyzing the communicative functions of aberrant behavior. Journal of the Association for Persons with Severe Handicaps, 9, 201-212.

Gardner, W. I. (1996). A contextual view of nonspecific behavioral symptoms in persons with a dual diagnosis: A psychological model for selecting and monitoring drug interventions. Psychology in Mental Retardation, 21(3), 6-11.

Gardner, W. I., Clees, T., & Cole, C. L. (1983). Self-management of disruptive verbal ruminations by a mentally retarded adult. Applied Research in Mental Retardation, 4, 41-58.

Gardner, W. I., & Cole, C. L. (1986). Aggression and related conduct difficulties. In J. Matson (Ed.), Handbook of behavior modification with the mentally retarded (pp. 225-254). New York: Plenum Press.

Gardner, W. I., & Cole, C. L. (1993). Aggression. In J. Matson & R. P. Barrett (Eds.), Psychopathology in the mentally retarded (2nd ed.) (pp. 213-252). Boston: Allyn & Bacon.

Gardner, W. I., & Cole, C. L. (1987). Behavior treatment, behavior management, and behavior control: Needed distinctions. Behavioral Residential Treatment, 2, 37-53.

Gardner, W. I., Cole, C. L., Davidson, D. P., & Karan, O. C. (1986). Reducing aggression in individuals with developmental disabilities: An expanded stimulus control, assessment, and intervention model. Education and Training of the Mentally Retarded, 21, 3-12.

Gardner, W. I., & Graeber, J. L. (1994). Use of behavioral therapies to enhance personal competencies. In N. Bouras (Ed.), Mental retardation and mental health - the way ahead (pp. 205-223). Cambridge: Cambridge University Press.

Gardner, W. I., Graeber, J. L., & Cole, C. L. (1996). Behavior therapies: A multimodal diagnostic and intervention model. In J. Jacobson & J. Mulick (Eds.), Manual of diagnosis and professional practice in mental retardation (pp. 355-369). Washington, DC: American Psychological Association.

Gardner, W. I., Graeber, J. L., & Ford, D. (in press). Behavior therapies: Individualizing interventions through treatment formulations. In A. Dosen and D. Day (Eds.), Handbook of treatment of mental illness and behavior disorders in children and adults with mental retardation. Washington, DC: American Psychiatric Press.

Gardner, W. I., & Sovner, R. (1994). Self-injurious behaviors, diagnosis and treatment, a multimodal approach. Willow Street, PA: VIDA Publishing.

Gardner, W. I., & Whalen, J. P. (1996). A multimodal behavior analytic model for evaluating the effects of medical problems on nonspecific behavioral symptoms in persons with developmental disabilities. Behavioral Interventions: Theory and Practice in Residential and Community-Based Clinical Programs, 11, 147-161.

Griffiths, D. (1984). DEINSTITUTIONALIZATION: The component of a value based system for planning and implementing the repatriation for persons with handicapping conditions. Toronto, Ontario: Ontario Association for the Mentally Retarded.

Griffiths, D. (1985). Pine Ridge: A follow up study one year later. Toronto, Ontario: Ontario Association for the Mentally Retarded.

Griffiths, D. (1998). Developing an habilitative home for persons with a developmental handicap and serious behavior problems. Manuscript submitted for publication.

Griffiths, D. (1989). Quality assurance for behavior interventions. Psychiatric Aspects of Mental Retardation Reviews, 8-11, 73-80.

Griffiths, D. (1990). Practical considerations for teaching social skills. Part II. Habilitative Mental Health Care Newsletter, 9, 9-13.

Griffiths, D. (in press). Strategic behavioral intervention of aggression. In A. Dosen and D. Day (Eds.), Handbook of treatment of mental illness and behavior disorders in children and adults with mental retardation. Washington, DC: American Psychiatric Press.

Griffith, D., Feldman, M. A., & Tough, S. (1997). Programming generalization of social skills in adults with developmental disabilities: Effects of generalization and social validity. Behavior Therapy, 28, 253-269.

Griffiths, D., Richards, D., & Fedoroff, P. (1998). Biomedical and psychosocial considerations of aggressive and destructive behavior. Manuscript submitted for publication.

Helmstetter, E., & Durand, V. M. (1990). Nonaversive interventions for severe behavior problems. In L. H. Meyer, C. A. Peck, & L. Brown (Eds.), Critical issues in the lives of people with severe disabilities (pp. 559-600). Baltimore: Paul H. Brookes.

Hingsburger, D. (1984). From culture to culture: Issues in deinstitutionalization. Richmond Hill, Ontario: Behavior Management Services, York Central Hospital.

Horner, R. H., & Day, H. M. (1991). The effects of response efficiency on functionally equivalent competing behaviors. Journal of Applied Behavior Analysis, 24, 719-732.

Koegel, L. K., Koegel, R. L., & Dunlap, G. (1996). Positive behavioral supports. Baltimore: Paul H. Brookes Publishing.

Lindsay, W. R., Howells, L., & Pitcaithly D. (1993). Cognitive therapy for depression with individuals with intellectual disabilities. British Journal of Medical Psychology, 66, 135-141.

Lowry, M. A. (1994). Functional assessment of problem behaviors associated with mood disorders. The Habilitative Mental Healthcare Newsletter, 13, 79-84.

Lowry, M. A., & Sovner, R. (1992). Severe behavior problems associated with rapid cycling bipolar disorder in two adults with profound mental retardation. Journal of Intellectual Disability Research, 36, 269-281.

Luiselli, J. K. (1996). Recent developments in the functional assessment and analysis of challenging behaviors. The Habilitative Mental Healthcare Newsletter, 15-4, 81-84.

Martens, B. K., & Witt, J. C. (1988). Ecological behavior analysis. In M. Hersen, R. M. Eisler, & P. M. Miller (Eds.), Progress in behavior modification (Vol. 22, pp. 115-140). Newbury Park, CA: Sage Publishing.

Nugent, J. (1994). A handbook on dual diagnosis: Supporting people with a developmental disability and a mental health problem. Mississauga, Ontario: Nugent Training & Consulting Services.

O'Neill, R. E., Horner, R. H., Albin, R. W., Storey, K., & Sprague, J. R. (1990). Functional analysis: A practical assessment guide. Sycamore, IL: Sycamore Publishing.

O'Reilly, M. F. (1995). Functional analysis and treatment of escape-maintained aggression correlated with sleep deprivation. Journal of Applied Behavior Analysis, 28, 225-226.

Peine, H. A., Darvish, R., Adams, K., Blakelock, H., Jenson, W., & Osborne, J. G. (1995). Medical problems, maladaptive behaviors and the developmentally disabled. Behavioral Interventions, 10, 149-159.

Pfadt, A., & Holburn, C. S. (1996). Community-based support services update. The Habilitative Mental Healthcare Newsletter, 15, 8-11.

Reese, R. M., Sherman, J. A., & Sheldon, J. (1984). Reducing agitated-disruptive behavior of mentally retarded residents of community group homes: The role of self-recording and peer-prompted self-recording. Analysis and Intervention in Developmental Disabilities, 4, 91-107.

Reiss, S. (1988). The Reiss Screen for Maladaptive Behavior: Test Manual. Worthington, OH: IDS Publications.

Reiss, S. (1994). Handbook of challenging behavior: Mental health aspects of mental retardation. Worthington, OH: International Diagnostic Systems.

Reiss, S., & Havercamp, S. M. (1997). Sensitivity theory and mental retardation: Why functional analysis is not enough. American Journal of Mental Retardation, 101, 553-566.

Renwick, R., Brown, I., & Raphael, D. (1994). Quality of life; linking a conceptual approach to service provision. Journal on Developmental Disabilities, 3(2), 32-44.

Rogers, C. (1972). My philosophy of interpersonal relationships and how It grew. Journal of Humanistic Psychology, 13(2), 12-19.

Smith, R. G., Iwata, B. A., Vollmer, T. R., & Zarcone, J. R. (1993). Experimental analysis and treatment of multiply controlled self-injury. Journal of Applied Behavior Analysis, 26, 183-196.

Sovner, R., Foxx, C. J., Lowry, M. J., & Lowry, M. A. (1993). Fluoxetine treatment of depression and associated self-injury in two adults with mental retardation. Journal of Intellectual Disabilities Research, 37, 301-311.

Thompson, T., Egli, M., Symons, F., & Delaney, D. (1994). Neurobehavioral mechanisms of drug action in developmental disabilities. In T. Thompson & D. B. Gray (eds.), Destructive behavior in developmental disabilities (pp. 133-180). Thousand Oaks, CA: Sage Publications.

Touchette, P. E., MacDonald, R. F., & Langer, S. N. (1985). A scatter plot for identifying stimulus control of problem behavior. Journal of Applied Behavior Analysis, 18, 343-351.

Turner, F. J., & Turner, J. C. (1985). Evaluation of the five year plan for the closure of mental retardation facilities, Southwest Region. Toronto, Ontario: the Ministry of Community and Social Services.

Tutt, R., & Osborne, J. (1983). The closing of St. Lawrence Regional Centre: lessons to be learned. Toronto, Ontario: Ontario Association for the Mentally Retarded.

Wolfensberger, W. (1972). The principle of normalization in human services. Toronto, Ontario: National Institute on Mental Retardation.

Zegiob, L., Klukas, N., & Junginger, J. (1978). Reactivity of self-monitoring procedures with retarded adolescents. American Journal of Mental Deficiency, 83, 156-163.

APPENDIX A

TEACHING SOCIAL SKILLS AS FUNCTIONAL REPLACEMENTS FOR CHALLENGING BEHAVIOR: A SOCIAL LIFE GAME

Dorothy M. Griffiths

Purpose

To teach prosocial skills as replacements for challenging behavior.

Method of Assessment

Results from the comprehensive case formulation should yield:

- The conditions that instigate the behavior.
- The skill deficits that contribute to the challenging behavior.
- The factors that maintain the behavior.

Based upon this formulation, prosocial skills are identified that could be used by the individual to:

- Remove, alter, or respond differently to the instigating factors.
- Serve as replacements for the challenging behavior.
- Gain desired reinforcement (positive or negative) through appropriate means.

Note: The social skill behaviors should be <u>relevant</u> to the individual. This means that the behaviors should provide the individual with an appropriate and effective means of avoiding the unpleasant events or gaining the pleasant event that maintain the challenging behavior. The support staff and the person with the challenging behavior must both agree that the new behaviors are relevant to reducing the challenging behavior.

The Social LIFE Approach

The Social LIFE game (described by Griffiths, 1990; Griffiths, Feldman, & Tough, 1997) provides a nonthreatening and highly effective method of teaching social skills. The game, developed by York Behaviour Management Services in Richmond Hill, Ontario, Canada, uses a modified Monopoly format. It consists of the modified board, a die, a playing piece for each player, at least 24 playing cards for each player, and reinforcers. The object of the game is to advance around the modified Monopoly board in a counter-clockwise direction, earning money in return for appropriate responses to the game cards. The participant with the most money at the end of the game is the winner. Additionally, each player exchanges their game money for a reinforcer at the end of the game. The board layout is depicted at the end of this Appendix.

Preparing the Cards

The game cards are developed by the trainer to reflect the specific replacement behaviors for each player. The facilitator should make up at least 24 cards (6 cards in each of the four categories) for each player. It is important to have multiple examples that represent situations the person may experience in daily life. The monetary value and content of each card are as follows:

- *Give and Take* Cards

> Each *Give and Take* card describes a social interaction that is appropriate or inappropriate. Examples: "You were introduced to a new woman in the residence and you shook her hand. Win $5.00." "You gave a hug to a stranger. Lose $5.00." The group would discuss why this would earn or lose you $5.00. Some people prefer only to use *Give or Take* cards that instruct appropriate behaviors. That may be preferable for some individuals. In this instance, the player could always earn $5.00 for a *Give and Take* card.

- *Right or Wrong* Cards

> *Right or Wrong* cards are worth $10.00. These cards make a statement to which the player has to judge it to be right or wrong. Example: "It is ok to hold hands with your girlfriend at work." The person must decide if this is a

correct or an incorrect way to behave. The group then discusses the player's response and decides if the answer that was given was correct and if the player should earn the $10.00.

- *Fill In Cards*

Fill In cards are worth $15.00. The player must complete the sentence correctly to earn the points. Example: "When I meet a new person I_____." The group discusses the response given and decides if the answer was correct and if the player should earn the $15.00.

- *Play A Role Cards*

Play a Role cards are worth $20.00. The person must act out a role-play with the mediator or one of the other players. Example: "Your roommate is angry with you. Show what you would do." " You are very angry. Show one way you would relax." It is best not to have a player role-play an inappropriate role. The group then discusses how the person responded to the situation and determines if the person should earn the $20.00.

Mr. Biggs provides an illustration:

Mr. Alex Biggs has a problem with anger. He gets very angry when he is corrected. He tends to throw things and get very disruptive. Here are some samples of Mr. Biggs cards:

- **Give and Take:** Although you feel like throwing a drinking glass because you are angry, you don't. Earn $5.00.

- **Right or Wrong:** Because your roommates throw things when they are angry, it is okay for you to throw things too. Is that right or wrong?

- **Fill In:** When you are angry at someone, instead of throwing something at them you should———.

- **Role Play:** You are doing dishes and Paula (a staff) says that you are not getting the dishes clean enough. Show how you would respond to Paula.

Rules of the Game

Colored side squares on the board are repeated in sets of four for each side of the board. Squares denote:

- **Red** : Give and Take
- **Green**: Right or Wrong
- **Yellow**: Fill In
- **Blue**: Play a Role

A role of the die indicates the number of squares advanced. If a player lands on one of the squares, a color-coded card is picked from a pack of 24 cards. As noted, points are based on the player providing an appropriate response to the problem posed. Play money is used unless the participants have difficulty with money concepts, and then poker chips can be used.

In addition to the colored squares there are bonus squares at the corners and in the center of each side. The four corner squares are *Vacation* (No value), *Go to Movies* (No value), *Out for Dinner* and *Payday* (get $50). The side squares are *Win a Lottery* ($100), *Sick, Lose Pay* (minus $20), *Pay Rent* (minus $100) and *Happy Birthday* (get $20). These squares add to the game-like atmosphere and increase motivation.

The game is played with four individuals, all of whom have different behavioral needs. This is important because players can model the range of appropriate behavior described on the cards. The players should all have a natural social relationship and interact regularly in order to facilitate generalization of skills learned. The criterion for being a player includes the ability to communicate and to learn to role-play.

Staff members with ongoing contact with the players in social situations should serve as the trainers/mediators. The staff member should know the players sufficiently well to be able to develop the cards for use in the game.

The game should be played in a natural environment such as the home, work, or school. The setting should be relatively comfortable and free from distractions.

The game board should be placed on a table and the game cards placed face down in piles in an allotted space in the center of the board. Each player starts out with $150 in play money. The trainer or one of the players can act as banker. The game begins with the person who roles the highest number on the die. The game players all start at Payday and move in a clock-wise direction.

Method of Instruction

The game provides an opportunity for the mediator to use instruction, performance feedback, positive reinforcement, modeling, repeated practice and role-playing. Participants should be rewarded throughout the game for participating and for appropriate responses. At the end of the game, the play dollars should be able to be exchanged for some reinforcement (such as going out for pizza). Reinforcers must be individually determined; however, social or group reinforcers are appropriate.

The game also provides an opportunity for players to provide feedback, to model, and to role-play appropriate responses for other players. Players also will observe other players being reinforced for giving an appropriate response to another person's problem. The person therefore acts as a model for other players.

The group dialogue can be used as an opportunity to discuss why a response might be correct or incorrect. Thus the players not only are learning a "discrete correct vs. incorrect" rule about social behavior but also the rationale for the appropriate behavior. In this way, the players are learning to be sensitized to the feelings of others and the impact their behavior has on the environment and their interactions with others.

The game is generally played for 6-8 weeks, playing once or twice a week, for 45 minutes to 60 minutes a game. Game cards can be added, deleted or changed as the game goes on to maintain interest, to develop new skills or to refine skills previously learned. The game is usually stopped when the players are able to achieve 80% or more on their own cards. The mediator should keep a record during the game of how the players did on their own cards.

Generalization

It really does not matter how well the person does in the game unless the new skills are used in current real life situations where they are needed. The mediator should observe and record whether the person is now using the new replacement skill in situations where a challenging behavior was previously exhibited.

There are ways that a mediator can assist in generalization. The individuals in the natural environment, including the other players of the game, can prompt the behavior to occur in situations, reinforce the new behavior, and redirect the person to use the new behavior at the onset of the challenging behavior.

> *Note: It is important that the new prosocial behavior be as effective and efficient at gaining positive or negative reinforcement as the challenging behavior. Otherwise, the behavior will soon fall into disuse and the challenging behavior will return in full force.*

The Social L.I.F.E. game was developed in 1979 by York Behaviour Management Services in Richmond Hill, Ontario, Canada.

APPENDIX B

TEACHING SKILLS OF SELF-MANAGEMENT

William I. Gardner

Observations of persons with mental retardation who also present chronic challenging behaviors suggest that many have personal characteristics or features that contribute to these behavioral difficulties. Many are excessively influenced by "outside" events that reside in their physical and social environments. Terms such as "dependent," "outer directed," and "having an external locus of control" have been used to describe their general demeanor. Many tend to be "reactive" in response to sources of aggravation or provocation rather than behaving in a reflective, thoughtful, or self-directed manner. The basic skills of self-managment are only partially developed and seldom are used in provocative situations that require self-control and self-direction to insure appropriate responding. As a result, many view themselves as being excessively controlled by others and as having only minimal influence or responsibility for their actions. The external nature of this control may be depicted as follows:

EXTERNAL CONTROL

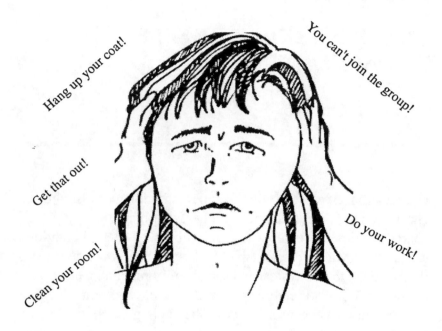

This appendix describes various skills of self-management that have been acquired and used successfully by persons with varying degrees of cognitive impairment. These skills, listed in Table 3, may be useful in shifting the locus of control *from* the support staff and others in the person's world *to* the person. In so doing, the person is moved from a state of relative dependency on others toward a state of increased independence and personal responsibility.

ANTECEDENTS	CONSEQUENCES

Self	-instruction (cueing)
	  -verbal
	  -pictorial
	  -prerecorded statements
		Self	-monitoring
			-observation
			-discrimination
			-recording

Self	-selection of consequences
	  -amount and type of reinforcers
	  -amount and type of negative
	    consequences
		Self
		Self
			-evaluation (assessment)
			-consequation (reinforcement;
			  punishment)

Self	-determined performance
	  criteria (standard setting)
		Self	-reinforcement
			  -administration of reinforers
			   selected by self
			  -administration of reinforcers
			   determined by others

		Self	-punishment
			  -administration of negative
			   consequences selected by self
			  -administration of negative
			   consequences determined
			   by others

Table 3. Self-Management Skills

Use of self-management procedures by support staff provides individual centered interventions that offer the potential for rapid reduction in a range of challenging behviors. While no one of us is totally independent of social supports, our level of independence is defined by the skillful use of the range of self-managment skills depicted above.

Self-management has reference to those behaviors engaged in by an individual (such as self-monitoring or self-instruction) that influence other of his own behaviors. With specific reference to challenging behaviors, self-managed interventions refer to the person doing something (the self-controlling response or action) that would change the likelihood of occurrence of a challenging behavior (the self-controlled behavior or action) that currently is under some other controlling influences. For example, a person who typically becomes angry and strikes out whenever a peer yells at him may self-control his striking out by self-prompting an alternative behavior such as ignoring the yelling, walking away from the peer, or enlisting the assistance of staff to assist in quieting his peer.

As noted in Table 3, these controlling self-management strategies include those that precede occurrence of a challenging behavior (behavioral antecedents) as well as those that follow occurrence of a challenging behavior (behavioral consequence). While all are useful in increasing the independence of the person and in reducing challenging behaviors, major attention in the following discussion is provided those self-managing skills of self-monitoring, self-evaluation, self-consequation, and self-cueing (aka self-talk, self-instruction). Each is described and illustrated.

Self-Monitoring

Self-monitoring, involving self-observation or self-discrimination of a target behavior followed by self-recording of this observation, has been demonstrated to produce therapeutic reactive effects with individuals with diverse personal characteristics and behaviors. That is, this simple act of self-recording a self-discriminated behavior may result in a change in the occurrence of the behavior.

Self-monitoring represents the intital self-management skill to be taught.The person after determining the occurrence or nonoccurrence of a specified behavior (or thought, or emotion) is taught to make a recording of this discrimination.

Training typically consists of teaching the person through verbal instruction, modeling, guided rehearsal, and feedback to identify the target behavior and to record each episode. Self-recording may involve paper-and-pencil procedures such as a note card, note book, or slip of paper on which the person makes a tally mark for each occurrence of the target behavior to more detailed and structured data forms as depicted below. Mechanical devices such as hand-held wrist and belt-worn counters also have been used successfully with persons with developmental disabilities. See Figure 3 for examples of various self-recording formats.

WEEKLY SCHEDULE

DAY	TASK	YES	NO	NOTES
SUNDAY				
MONDAY				
TUESDAY				
WEDNESDAY				
THURSDAY				
FRIDAY				
SATURDAY				

Place a check in a box each time you initiate talk with a peer.

TALKING	NO TALKING
🙂	☹️

DAILY SCHEDULE

TIME	TASK	YES	NO	NOTES

BUS RIDING SKILLS DATA SHEET

Name _____   Date _____

	YES	NO
1. I stood at bus stop. 2. I ignored strangers at bus stop. 3. I knew my bus. 4. I waited until my bus stopped. 5. I walked up the stairs. 6. I put money in slot or showed my ID card to driver. 7. I asked for transfer. 8. I walked to empty seat and sat down or stood holding handbars. 9. I ignored stranger on bus. 10. I rang bell when I wanted to get off the bus. 11. I sat down until the bus stopped. 12. I walked to the closest door. 13. I waited for the door to open or pushed open door. 14. I stepped down the stairs.		

Figure 3. Examples of Self-Monitoring Formats

As an example of self-monitoring, an adolescent with mild cognitive impairment was trained to use a pencil and index card to record occurrences of self-injurious behaviors (Zegiob, Klukas, & Junginger, 1978). Reese, Sherman, and Sheldon (1984) trained a 22-year-old female to self-record occurrence/nonoccurrence of incidents of agitated disruptive behaviors (e.g., yelling, cursing, kicking and banging and throwing objects, attacking staff) during designated time intervals. She was provided a pocket timer and a recording sheet on which was listed the agitated disruptive behaviors and a column of time intervals. Next to each time interval, marked off in hours, were two blanks labeled either "Handled my temper" or "I lost my temper." After having been taught to set the pocket timer, the woman was instructed to mark her sheet in the appropriate blank when the timer sounded. As a final example of self-recording, Cole and Gardner (1990) trained a 36-year-old woman with a dual diagnosis of mild mental retardation and thought disorder associated with schizophrenia to self-assess and self-record occurrences of disruptive verbal behaviors in a vocational setting. The behaviors involved talking aloud to herself in a disorganized, rambling manner (e.g., "You should never be mad on Main Street," "I'm going to die a young girl," "I'm going to call the cops and have you arrested!"). This disruptive self-talk occurred out of context and had not responded positively to other behavioral interventions. In the work setting, when staff attempted to label her behavior and redirect her, she often became increasingly upset. She occasionally escalated into episodes of screaming, crying, threatening, and swearing. On most occasions, she responded appropriately to actual events or situations in the work environment. Training in self-assessment and recording initially was provided in a therapy room away from the work setting and later moved onto the work floor. She was provided a small speaker on her work table that would emit, about every 10-minutes, a tone. After the tone, she was taught to ask herself, "Was I talking or not talking?" and to record her decision on a prepared recording sheet located at her work station. (The recording sheet used is depicted in Figure 3.)

As noted in the examples above, self-monitoring is useful as a method of getting information about the occurrence/nonoccurrence of a specific behavior. In addition, Lindsay, Howells, and Pitcaithly (1993) trained persons with mild cognitive impairment to self-assess and self-record the amount that each person worried each day. An analogue scale for worry which incorporated daily ratings and descriptive histograms to assist in the persons's ratings

was used. The person was taught that the low bar indicates no
worry, the intermediate histogram indicates greater degrees of
worry and the largest histogram indicates a great deal of worry
during the day. An illustration of this scale is as follows:

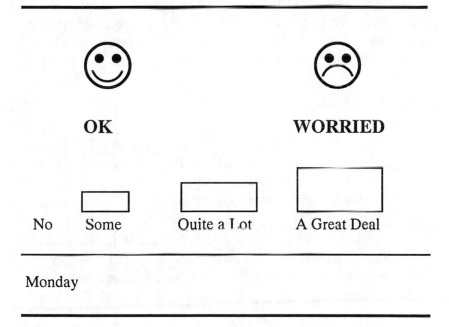

Therapeutic Effects of Self-Monitoring

As noted earlier, self-monitoring may be useful in encouraging
positive behavior changes. In illustration, self-monitoring may be
used to increase desired behaviors that do occur but at a level
lower than desired. As an example, a person with mild symptoms
of depression who is isolating herself from social contact may be
requested to self-record each occasion of initiating social interactions with peers or staff. Self-monitoring also may be result in a
decrease in the frequency of undesired behaviors. In the studies

described previously (Cole & Gardner, 1990; Reese et al., 1984; Zegiob et al., 1978), the challenging behaviors that were self-recorded all decreased in a clinically significant manner. Even though clinical experience with self-monitoring with persons with mental retardation and challenging behavior indicates that the level of positive effects on the behavior being monitored is greater for persons who express a desire or commitment to change their behaviors, it also is evident that persons who are relatively unconcerned over their problem behaviors respond positively.

Self-Evaluation

After the person has become skillful in self-monitoring his/her own behaviors (both prosocial and challenging behaviors), the skill of self-evaluating the behavior against various standards of conduct is taught. These standards of conduct may represent a range of expected conduct based on various legal, social, developmental, house rules, family values, ethical and religious beliefs, and the like. The types of behavioral expectations, of course, vary across setting and conditions. To illustrate, some behaviors would be viewed as appropriate in a leisure setting but not appropriate in a work setting.

Persons with developmental disabilities and mental health concerns frequently experience difficulty in "knowing" what is expected or, even if able to verbalize what is expected, is unable to use this knowledge to self-evaluate their own actions against these expectation or standards. It thus becomes necessary initially to specify in terms understandable to the person the specfic standards or rules that the persons is expected to meet.

As an example of standards of conduct against which persons can assess and evaluate their own actions, a group home serving persons with mental retardation and severely challenging behaviors identified the following personal/social behavioral standards expected of persons residing in the home:

- Adults follow their daily schedule.
- Adults maintain self-control when angry or upset.
- Adults respect other people.
- Adults are responsible for their own space and personal belongings.

Each person was taught through group discussion, role play, and feedback the more specific behaviors involved in each of these general standards of conduct. As illustration, for the standard Adults Maintain Self-Control When Angry or Upset, the person was taught coping behaviors via group role play and feedback that when they become excessively angry or upset to:

- Take a deep breath and walk away.
- Take a deep breath and talk calmly.
- Ignore inappropriate behaviors of others.
- Take a deep breath and listen to support staff.

Further, these coping behaviors were taught under the following conditions that most frequently preceded challenging behaviors:

- When someone is yelling at you.
- When someone bosses you around.
- When someone teases you.
- When someone takes something away from you.
- When others are upset.
- When someone directs you to do something that you do not wish to do.

With this standard-setting and training in desired coping behaviors, the person is in a position to self-evaluate his/her behavior as "Appropriate or Inappropriate," or "Used Self-Control or Did Not Use Self-Control." Staff also is in a position following a specific incident to ask: "Susan, what did you do when John teased you?" "Was that Using Self-Control of Not Using Self-Control?"

As is evident, self-evaluation typically is used in combination with other procedures. As an example, Gardner, Clees, and Cole (1983) demonstrated with an adult with severe problems of conduct that self-monitoring and self-evaluation reduced high rate disruptive vocalizations (verbal ruminations and nonspeech sounds) in a vocational training setting. Figure 4 provides an example of a format for self-monitoring and self-evaluation of various specific behaviors and classes of behaviors.

TOKEN PROGRAM			
NAME:			
EXPECTED BEHAVIORS			
1. Showed respect for the rights of others (i.e., did not threaten others). 2. Showed respect for the rights of others (i.e., did not engage in disruptive behaviors). 3. Showed respect for the personal integrity of others (i.e., was not physically aggressive). 4. Showed respect for own health (i.e., did not engage in self abuse).			
DATE	Reinforcement Times		
MONDAY			
TUESDAY			
WEDNESDAY			
THURSDAY			
FRIDAY			
SATURDAY			
SUNDAY			

At designated times review with _____ the expected behaviors. If he has been successful in each of these areas during the designated periods,_____ will mark his card. Provide enthusiastic feedback.

Figure 4: Example of Self-Evaluation Format

Self-Consequation

The next skill of self-consequation refers to the self-delivery of positive consequences (self-reinforcement) or negative consequences (self-punishment) following specific behaviors that have been self-evaluated as positive or negative. As an example, Cole, Gardner, and Karan (1985) taught adults with severe and chronic disruptive behaviors to reinforce themselves with money following periods of satisfactory work and absence of disruptive acts. This self-consequation followed self-monitoring and self-evaluation of "Adult Worker Behavior." Disruptive behaviors decreased significantly and production increased following use of these self-management procedures.

Self-Instruction

A critical self-management skill taught is that of self-talk. This self-talk or self-instruction is used to initiate, direct, or maintain prosocial alternatives to challenging behaviors. This self-talk can occur prior to or following occurrence of the challenging behaviors. In illustration, a person may be taught, upon detecting that he is becoming angry and feels like hitting his peer, to say to himself, "Just cool it. Don't get upset. Don't hit. Just walk away." "Jerry's teasing me, but I won't yell at him. I'm an adult and can control myself. I'll ignore him." In other instances, the person may be taught to anticipate situations in which challenging behaviors are likely to occur and to self-instruct an alternative coping behavior.

Self-Management Packages

Self-management training typically combines a variety of therapy procedures. Cole et al. (1985) illustrated this in a treatment program designed to reduce the high rate disruptive behaviors of six adults with mild to moderate cognitive impairment. All persons presented chronic and severe behavioral/emotional difficulties. Although each had been provided a range of psychiatric and psychological treatment, none had demonstrated desired progress. In fact, for all persons, clinically significant conduct difficulties had resulted in dismissal from, or precluded placement in, community vocational rehabilitation programs. Disruptive verbal and physical behaviors specific to each person served as treatment targets.

Each person was provided training in self-monitoring, self-evaluation and self-consequation of presence/absence of the challenging behaviors. Following demonstration of these skills each person was provided more detailed self-instructional training. Video and audio tapes of specific provocative situations (e.g., peer taunting, staff corrective feedback) were presented. The trainer modeled appropriate self-verbalizations in the presence of these instigating events (e.g., "Don't listen to her. Look away and ignore her."). Later the person was prompted by staff to use these statements to self-direct his or her appropriate behavior. During behavior rehearsal, the duration and intensity of the simulated provocation was gradually increased and the person was encouraged to speak more and more softly, with the ultimate goal of subvocal self-talk under actual provocation. Following individual training, each person resumed working in the vocational training setting. Each person initially was encouraged frequently to self-instruct and rehearse appropriate coping responses. These

staff prompts were gradually faded as the person became successful in independent self-management.

This intervention package with a major emphasis on self-management produced immediate and clinically significant reductions in
severe conduct difficulties in all six persons served. Nine-month
follow-up under different work conditions revealed continued
maintenance of treatment gains.

Summary

Clinical experiences suggest that persons with mental retardation
and significant challenging behaviors typically have minimal
skills of self-management. The person is excessively under the
influence of external provocation and behaves in an impulsive
manner to these. Both research and clinical experiences have
demonstrated that challenging behaviors can be reduced and the
person's independence can be enhanced by teaching skills of self-
management.

APPENDIX C

MULTIMODAL INTEGRATED INTERVENTION PLAN: A QUALITY ASSURANCE CHECKLIST

William I. Gardner

Individual: _____

Date: _____   **Staff:** _____

I: Identification of Challenging Behavior(s)

Yes No

__ __   a) Are the specific challenging behaviors clearly identified?

__ __   b) Do the behavior warrant intervention?

II: Diagnostic-Intervention Formulations

A: Medical

__ __   a)   Are medical diagnostic formulations concerning possible instigating, vulnerability, and/or maintaining influences included?

_____ _____ b) Are these keyed to specific challenging behaviors?

_____ _____ c) Are program objectives stated for each diagnostic formulation?

_____ _____ d) For each diagnostic formulation, is there a related intervention based on this diagnostic formulation?

_____ _____ e) Is there a staging plan that interfaces medical interventions with those of a psychiatric, psychological, and environmental nature?

_____ _____ f) Is there a statement specifying the type and magnitude of change expected in the challenging behaviors?

_____ _____ g) Is there a statement specifying the time within which a change in the challenging behaviors should be expected?

_____ _____ h) Is the type of data needed to evaluate the effects of the medical intervention on specific challenging behaviors specified?

_____ _____ i) Is the schedule of obtaining these data specified?

_____ _____ j) Is the staff responsible for gathering and reviewing these data specified?

_____ _____ k) Is the medical staff responsible for delivering and monitoring medical intervention(s) specified?

___ ___ l)   When changes are made in the intervention plan, are these based on new or revised diagnostic formulations?

___ ___ m)   If the intervention is being discontinued because of lack of success, have the reasons for the lack of effectiveness been analyzed and documented?

B: Psychiatric

___ ___ a)   Are psychiatric diagnostic formulations concerning possible instigating, vulnerability, and/or maintaining influences included?

___ ___ b)   Are these keyed to specific challenging behaviors?

___ ___ c)   Are program objectives stated for each diagnostic formulation?

___ ___ d)   For each diagnostic formulation, is there a related intervention based on this diagnostic formulation?

___ ___ e)   Is there a staging plan that interfaces psychiatric interventions with those of a medical, psychological, and environmental nature?

___ ___ f)   Is there a statement specifying the type and magnitude of change expected in the challenging behaviors?

_____ _____ g)   Is there a statement specifying the time within which a change in the challenging behaviors should be expected?

_____ _____ h)   Is the type of data needed to evaluate the effects of the psychiatric intervention on specific challenging behaviors specified?

_____ _____ i)   Is the schedule of obtaining these data specified?

_____ _____ j)   Is the staff responsible for gathering and reviewing these data specified?

_____ _____ k)   Is the staff responsible for delivering and monitoring psychiatric intervention(s) specified?

_____ _____ l)   When changes are made in the intervention plan, are these based on new or revised diagnostic formulations?

_____ _____ m)   If the intervention is being discontinued because of lack of success, have the reasons for the lack of effectiveness been analyzed and documented?

C. Psychological

_____ _____ a)   Are psychological diagnostic formulations concerning possible instigating, vulnerability, and/or maintaining influences included?

_____ _____ b)   Are these keyed to specific challenging behaviors?

___ ___ c)   Are program objectives stated for each diagnostic formulation?

___ ___ d)   For each diagnostic formulation, is there a related intervention based on this diagnostic formulation?

___ ___ e)   Is there a staging plan that interfaces psychological interventions with those of a medical, psychiatric, and environmental nature?

___ ___ f)   Is there a statement specifying the type and magnitude of change expected in the challenging behaviors?

___ ___ g)   Is there a statement specifying the time within which a change in the challenging behaviors should be expected?

___ ___ h)   Is the type of data needed to evaluate the effects of the psychological intervention on specific challenging behaviors specified?

___ ___ i)   Is the schedule of obtaining these data specified?

___ ___ j)   Is the staff responsible for gathering and reviewing these data specified?

___ ___ k)   Is the staff responsible for delivering and monitoring psychological intervention(s) specified?

___ ___ l)   When changes are made in the intervention plan, are these based on new or revised diagnostic formulations?

__ __ m)   If the intervention is being discontinued because of lack of success, have the reasons for the lack of effectiveness been analyzed and documented?

D. Environmental

__ __ a)   Are environmental diagnostic formulations concerning possible instigating, vulnerability, and/or maintaining influences included?

__ __ b)   Are these keyed to specific challenging behaviors?

__ __ c)   Are program objectives stated for each diagnostic formulation?

__ __ d)   For each diagnostic formulation, is there a related intervention based on this diagnostic formulation?

__ __ e)   Is there a staging plan that interfaces environmental interventions with those of a medical, psychiatric, and psychological nature?

__ __ f)   Is there a statement specifying the type and magnitude of change expected in the challenging behaviors?

__ __ g)   Is there a statement specifying the time within which a change in the challenging behaviors should be expected?

_____ _____ h) Is the type of data needed to evaluate the effects of the environmental intervention on specific challenging behaviors specified?

_____ _____ i) Is the schedule of obtaining these data specified?

_____ _____ j) Is the staff responsible for gathering and reviewing these data specified?

_____ _____ k) Is the staff responsible for delivering and monitoring environmental intervention(s) specified?

_____ _____ I) When changes are made in the inervention plan, are these based on new or revised diagnostic formulations?

_____ _____ m) If the intervention is being discontinued because of lack of success, have the reasons for the lack of effectiveness been analyzed and documented?

Summary

Answers to all of the questions listed above should be Yes. A "No" response would indicate gaps in the comprehensive behavior support plan.

Author Index

Subject Index

NADD Press Publications

Assessment and Treatment of Anxiety Disorders
Ann R. Poindexter, M.D. (Ed.), 1996

Behavioral Supports: Individual Centered Interventions
Dorothy M. Griffiths PhD.; William I. Gardner, PhD.; and
JoAnne Nugent, M.A. (Eds.), 1998

Effective Therapy Approaches for Persons with Intellectual Disabilities
Robert J. Fletcher, D.S.W., A.C.S.W., (Ed.), 1999

Habilitative Neuropsychiatry: Psychopharmacology (1985-1986) A Reference Guide
Jeffery J. Fahs, M.D.

*Look for future NADD Press publications
on these related topics:*

Aggression
William I. Gardner, PhD. (Ed.)

Psychopharmacology
Earl Loschen, M.D. (Ed.)

Program Models
John Jacobson, Ph.D. (Ed.)

Older Adults
Robert Pary, M.D. (Ed.)

Staff Training
Donna McNelis, Ph.D.

**For information about obtaining these books
or information about NADD contact:**

 An association for persons with
developmental disabilities and
mental health needs.

132 Fair St., Kingston, NY 12401-4802
Phone (914) 331-4336   (800)331-5362   Fax (914) 331-4569   E-mail: thenadd@aol.com
or visit us on the web at:

www.thenadd.org